A Story Based on True Events

Spaghetti in a Suitcase

My Journey to the Seychelles

GW00381208

Felice Soru

Felix Publishing

ISBN-978-1-7397720-3-1

"The wind of change is blowing through this continent, and whether we like it or not, this growth of national consciousness is a political fact.
We must all accept it as a fact, and our national policies must take account of it."

Harold Macmillan, South Africa, 3 February 1960

"When a man is no longer faithful to his purpose, destiny deserts him."

A wise man

To Helena, with love always and more.
A special thanks to my daughter Cristina for initial inspiration
and encouragement.

Contents

Chapter one	A Tranquil Town	1
Chapter two	Pioneering and Beyond	6
Chapter three	Seicelle	16
Chapter four	The Entrepreneur's Residence	19
Chapter five	The Governor	22
Chapter six	Planning My Trip	27
Chapter seven	The Outbound Journey	29
Chapter eight	The Seychelles	32
Chapter nine	Landing in Mahé	35
Chapter ten	Yellow Mini Moke	39
Chapter eleven	The Drive into Victoria	41
Chapter twelve	The Company's Office	45
Chapter thirteen	Making New Friends	49
Chapter fourteen	Permit to Work	51
Chapter fifteen	New Duties	53
Chapter sixteen	Praslin, Christmas 1977	55
Chapter seventeen	Becoming Inseparable	58
Chapter eighteen	Local Infrastructure	61
Chapter nineteen	A Pot Pourri of Flavours	63
Chapter twenty	Socialist Vision	67
Chapter twenty one	Laissez Faire	70
Chapter twenty two	The Uniqueness of an Island	72
Chapter twenty three	Helena's Brother	80
Chapter twenty four	Nello Africanus	83
Chapter twenty five	The Bird Sanctuary Island, Easter 1978	87
Chapter twenty six	The Sardinian Robinson Crusoe	89
Chapter twenty seven	The Glitzy Party	94
Chapter twenty eight	A Mysterious Guest	96
Chapter twenty nine	The New Co-owner	101
Chapter thirty	Time to Split the Group	103
Chapter thirty one	A Break from Paradise, July 1978	105
Chapter thirty two	East Africa Adventure, Christmas 1978	111
Chapter thirty three	A Resourceful Lady	114

Chapter thirty four	A House at St Louis	117
Chapter thirty five	In Charge of Operations, February 1979	120
Chapter thirty six	The Birthday	123
Chapter thirty seven	Air Seychelles	125
Chapter thirty eight	Underground Resistance	127
Chapter thirty nine	The Bigarade Island, Easter 1979	130
Chapter forty	Welcome Elixir, July 1979	135
Chapter forty one	Manipulation	137
Chapter forty two	The Slow Pace	139
Chapter forty three	Professor Palmieri	141
Chapter forty four	Refusal to Exit	144
Chapter forty five	Threats and Intimidation	146
Chapter forty six	The Far East Expedition, November 1980	148
Chapter forty seven	Short of Cash	151
Chapter forty eight	Mercenaries	153
Chapter forty nine	Isolated	160
Chapter fifty	A Fishing Expedition	163
Chapter fifty one	Back to his Farmhouse	170
Chapter fifty two	Unresolved Issues	172
Chapter fifty three	To Freedom	174
Chapter fifty four	The Morning of Thursday, 12 July 1982	178
Chapter fifty five	The Mutineers	180
Chapter fifty six	Eroded Friendship	183
Chapter fifty seven	A New Venture	185
Chapter fifty eight	To Fly International	188
Chapter fifty nine	Moving to England	190
Chapter sixty	Coup Attempt	195
Chapter sixty one	Maintaining Power	197
Chapter sixty two	Air Sardinia	201
Chapter sixty three	Italia 1990	204
Chapter sixty four	Betrayed	206
Chapter sixty five	Mama's Spaghetti	209

Chapter one

A Tranquil Town

I was born in Terralba, a tranquil town just a few miles from the west coast of the Italian island of Sardinia. The town was quite lively and liberal compared to the way of life on the rest of Sardinia, which remains archaic.

With a population of just over 10,000, Terralba mostly relied on its agricultural resources for its wealth, with vineyards, grains and vegetable produce giving its citizens a reasonable standard of living.

Back in the day, the town featured three cinemas and two discotheques. People from nearby villages would convene there during the week for shopping and during the weekends for amusement and entertainment. During the summer season in particular, the town would come alive as emigrants and their families returned for the holidays.

On Sundays and feast days, the main street was dressed up with colourful flags and glittering lights. A row of stalls would be set up, selling a variety of local products: *pecorino* cheeses, *salciccia*, homemade *torrone*, sweets and cakes. Aromatic herbs that had been scattered on the ground during the saint's procession earlier in the day crunched underfoot, diffusing its perfume into the air, while families and couples perused the stalls.

In the still warm evening air, the piazza, along with its cathedral, would be filled up with locals and outsiders dressed in their best clothes for the evening *passeggiata*, during which they could wind down from the day's heat, and perhaps sample a delicious *gelato*. The older locals would pick on the strangers, questioning their presence: 'Who is that? What are they doing here?' Curiosity and gossip were a major pastime for them. Such questions would form the topic of discussion and chitchat the following morning among friends gathering for morning coffee at the bar. Everybody loved a bit of gossip. Throughout the summer, the town had a packed schedule of events and traditional religious feasts that locals would not want to miss out on. Life in town was entirely predictable and peaceful.

Mama was a strong lady. In her late fifties, she had raised four sons almost on her own, as Babbu had spent most of his working life away from home. Growing up after the war had been hard and losing her father when she was eight years old had made her tough and resilient. In her teens, she had moved to her aunt's house to work as a housekeeper in order to provide for her family. My parents had a stable routine; both were up and on the go before dawn.

Mama's duties would commence as soon as she put on one of her homemade dark-coloured aprons. Her work usually lasted from dawn to dusk, except for outings and at lunch break for a siesta. She loved cross-stitching tapestry in any spare time available to her, creating beautiful pieces based on traditional Sardinian designs. Her unique pieces were never for sale but shared throughout the family.

She was well organised with all her housework, from the cooking to the cleaning, but most of all she was dedicated to looking after the family. Nothing was too much for her. She never said she was tired, and never complained or moaned; we always came first. Every morning, as well as preparing breakfast, she would start making the meals for the day, putting pasta sauces or minestrone on the stove. She was a fantastic cook. And she was in charge; we had a matriarchal society after all! She was the pillar of the family.

Babbu retired early from his job as an irrigation systems technician following a knee injury and dedicated himself fulltime to the vineyards he owned. It was laborious work, as the entire growth cycle was overseen manually, using the traditional ways of our ancestors. His routine would begin every morning, when he cycled to one of his vineyards to tend to it until it was too hot to continue, before returning home after his early morning work to eat lunch and take a siesta. Later in the afternoon, as the heat died down, he would visit the piazza and meet with friends for the day's gossip, returning home just before dinnertime.

My parents had been happily married for over forty years. The family was expected to help Babbu work the vineyards throughout the year and all of us helped with the September harvest. Babbu had an authoritarian approach to both his family and work life; I was the youngest of his four children, so he exercised his will on me more strongly than I wanted him to! At times, I resented his attitude towards me and occasionally his strict ways hit me hard. Everyone at home respectfully addressed him with 'vostei', Sardinia's formal 'you' as a form of obedience. When I addressed him informally as 'tui', it did not make him happy. One day, when I was in my early teens, he confronted me and said, 'how dare you disrespect me by not addressing me with vostei?' Now, I was in turbulent waters! He waited for an answer. I got scared, suddenly fearful of the almost guaranteed telling off I would receive, along with a slap around the head. I tried to remain calm and, casually shrugging, replied that 'vostei' was an old-fashioned way to address a father, and 'tui' was the modern way to address a dad. It was not an attempt to be disrespectful, but a display of affection. He looked at me, puzzled, apparently searching intensely for an answer to my comment; perhaps my argument had appealed to his soft side as, on that occasion, I got away with it.

I always had the support of Mama but sometimes, understandably, even she had to back off. Most of all, I hated spending mornings at the vineyards during my school summer holiday.

I was seventeen and my school had just closed their doors for the summer holidays. Babbu sent me to hoe one of the vineyards. He told me at dinner that evening that if I had not finished the work, I would have to return the following morning. Mama woke me up at the crack of dawn the next day. Babbu had already gone to tend to another vineyard. I ate my breakfast, tied a hoe to my bicycle frame and off I went, pedalling along the country lane to the vineyard. The freshness of the morning was perfumed with the strong anise scent of wild fennel in the roadside hedges and I was overcome by the fragrance of wildflowers. The cactus trees, which were used as hedges to delimit the various vineyard properties, were bearing their prickly pear fruit. In different states of maturity, they were an array of colours, from dark green to a deep shade of cardinal red.

We had to take advantage of the coolness of the morning to work in the open fields. At ten, the sun was already high and hot, and we would come back home for lunch to avoid being burnt. When I arrived back at home that day, Babbu had already returned and was waiting for me.

In an angry tone, he accusingly asked me where I had been. He had passed by the vineyard and had not seen me there. I tried to remain calm, knowing better than to react badly lest I risked getting a smack. Then, suddenly the misunderstanding became clear; I had gone to the wrong field. He had wanted me at another site. He would not accept my mistake and ordered me to get on my bike immediately and go to the vineyard that he had intended for me to work on that morning. I was terribly upset with him, and Mama had not come to my aid.

Reluctantly, I got on the bike and off I went again. This was not the time to be at the vineyard and the heat of late morning was bearing down upon on me. The vines sprouted long, fresh shoots that reached out in all directions. They had already been finely trimmed to a certain height and width so that they formed perfectly straight hedgerows. They were just a little shorter than I was and created a row of maze-like, lemon-yellow bushes. Clusters of grapes were hanging from the still-tender branches.

The sky was blue and limpid, with not a single cloud. It was exceptionally calm, and the wind was silent and motionless: a sultry day. There was no place to hide from the scorching heat; even the lizards who were normally skulking around the land for prey took cover from the burning sun.

Every time I struck my hoe into the dry, difficult terrain, a mixture of pebble and sand, a cloud of dust would rise slowly from the ground. Every movement I made caused the dusty cloud around me to get bigger, until I was so engulfed by it that I could no longer see my tool hitting the soil. I perspired heavily, sweat dripping from my forehead, down my face, tracing lines down my neck before hitting the ground. The combination of sweat and dust darkened my uncovered skin. My t-shirt was soaked through and sticking to me unpleasantly. I was furious, swearing and cursing Babbu. The heat was becoming unbearable, and I had to take cover. I decided to return home.

It was long past midday, almost one o'clock, when I checked the old kitchen clock above the fireplace. I expected some more telling off from my father for having returned without finishing the job. I had already decided that I resolutely hated working at the vineyards and needed to look for a summer job to avoid further conflict. Mama was waiting for me; Babbu had already had his lunch and retired for his afternoon siesta. I had a cool shower followed by lunch with Mama. She sensed my teenage angst and I told her about my plan to find a summer job away from the vineyards, to which she reluctantly agreed.

Chapter two

Pioneering and Beyond

Ten miles away from town, there was a seaside hotel, the Ala Birdi. I knew that they were recruiting for the summer season, so I drove there that very afternoon on my run-down but faithful Lambretta. After a brief meeting, I managed to get myself a position as a commis waiter at the hotel restaurant, starting the next day. When I told Babbu, he reluctantly accepted the situation, although I could sense that he was not too pleased with my initiative. Just like that, I secured my first paid summer job, which afforded me a little more independence.

Like all Mediterranean islands, the bulk of tourism in Sardinia happens between April and September, thanks to the guaranteed good weather that the island is blessed with. Consequently, the locals lived on a six-month rotation, with the island coming to life in the sunshine, ready to welcome the influx of tourists. I was excited to be a part of it. It turned out that I really loved working at the hotel. Every day there would be new guests to meet, people from places all over Europe, each with their own customs and stories to tell. It allowed me to practice the French I had learned in school, and I improved quickly. The hours were long, but it did not feel like work to me, as I basked in the glamorous ambience that all the holidaymakers created. And how generously they tipped! The job turned out to be very financially rewarding, and by the end of the season, I had built up a cool amount of cash to support myself throughout the coming year of college in Cagliari.

The following summer, I took a job at one of the new hotels in Baja Sardinia, on the northeast of the island. The resort was next door to Porto Cervo, along the Costa Smeralda (the Emerald Coast). This was a newly developed project, funded by the Aga Khan; it was set to become the most fashionable destination for the rich and famous in the Mediterranean.

It felt like we were centre stage, pioneers in the new world of tourism. I was in a completely different Sardinia to the one I had grown up in; it was a foreign land compared to my sleepy hometown in the south-west. After work I made the most of the nightlife, rubbing shoulders with the glitterati and celebrities at exclusive and fashionable discotheques like Ritual and the Perroquet in Baja Sardinia. When the season ended and the tourists went home, I too returned to Terralba for the September harvest before heading back to college. However, I was left wanting more; the experience felt like the tip of the iceberg, and it had only fortified my thirst for adventure.

After what felt like an agonising wait, through a relatively unremarkable winter and spring, the summer of 1973 rolled around, and a new opportunity came knocking. A cousin invited me to visit him in England during my three-month summer college break. Having never left Sardinia before, I jumped at the chance. London at this time had become the centre of a youth revolution. The United Kingdom had just joined the European Economic Community (EEC) and travelling in and out without obstacle was now permitted for Europeans.

The most traveling I had done in my life up to that point had been the daily two-hour trips each way to my college campus in Cagliari. Together with two fellow students, we amused ourselves on the journey, goofing around to kill the boredom. Most days we would all bring food and dine together on the train. It was all improvised with whatever we managed to bring from home, such as pecorino, *pane carasau*, olives, *salciccia*, fresh artichokes, *finocchi* and wine. Not quite as luxurious as you would get on the Orient Express, but it was a lot of fun, and sometimes fellow passengers joined in on the experience!

A trip to England was something else altogether. I was going to travel from an island in the middle of Mediterranean Sea, through Europe, to another island across the English Channel. It started with a train ride to Porto Torres, then a ten-hour overnight ferry crossing to Genoa, all the while feeling seasick, before arriving in mainland Italy. On the train to Milan, I recovered from my seasickness and my appetite kicked in; thankfully Mama had prepared some *panini* for the journey. I remember enjoying my large *tartaruga* (a tortoise-shaped panino) filled with *melanzane*, soft cheese and chicken breast in breadcrumbs, the combination giving the *panino* just the right texture. At Milan Centrale, I had to wait hours for the night train to Calais. Once on board, I sat pensively by the window on the train, marvelling as humans do at the distance I was travelling, and appreciating the changes in temperature and scenery, as well as my fellow travellers and their gradual alterations in accents and clothing. I thought of my grandparents, who loved to say a particular Sardo proverb any time we took a trip to the next village or town, '*tanti ca sesi andendi a Londra*', which roughly translates to, 'you're just going out of Terralba, not to London!' But now I was on a train, actually on my way there! I felt fortunate.

Fearing theft, I remained in my compartment, dozing off now and then, and nibbling intermittently on my remaining *panino*. We eventually reached Calais and crossed the channel to Dover. I arrived at Victoria Station a little over three days after I had left Sardinia and was picked up by a cousin I hardly knew, who lived in Luton.

Luton was not exactly what I would describe as exciting for a teenager in search of adventure and discovery. It was described as an egalitarian place because of the diverse nationalities of people who lived there. It was also an industrious town that housed several car manufacturers and textile factories. My cousin was working for Chrysler at their plant in Dunstable, and he managed to get me a job there working on the assembly line on a night shift, for the duration of my stay. Luton was well connected with London, and my cousin's family welcomed me there with open arms, filling my stay with sightseeing on the weekends.

Luton airport became my main attraction. It was the base of several charter airline companies such as Britannia, Monarch and Court Line. Together with the tour operator, they were pioneering the new package holidays, which made travel affordable for the masses and allowed them holidays abroad for the first time.

I was fascinated by such an operation; a new world of travel had taken off. At every opportunity I would visit the airport and monitor departures and arrivals, paying close attention to the aircraft type and the airline companies.

At the end of my stay, I managed to book a reasonably priced air ticket to return to Italy on one of these flights. It was a Britannia Airways Boeing 737 from Luton Airport to Rome Ciampino airport; back then, there was no direct flight to Sardinia.

My cousin's family came to see me off. An entirely different boy stood before them compared to the one they had received just a few months prior. Having become intoxicated by British fashion, I had grown long hair with sideburns and was sporting bell bottoms. On the flight, I sat at my window seat and soaked up the views, savouring every moment of the two hours and thirty minutes it took to reach Rome.

When I returned to school that autumn, I caused quite a stir among my school mates, who were impressed by my new look and wanted to hear all the details of my experience abroad. None of them had ever travelled that far but we all shared the same starry-eyed views of London.

In July 1974, I completed my final exams and graduated as

a Technical Engineer at Cagliari College, before deciding shortly afterwards to return to England. I enrolled at the Luton Technology College and got a job at Caesar's Palace Casino as a waiter to support myself. This would be the longest I had been away from Terralba: almost a year and half. After my initial excitement at being back there disappeared, I found the English winter to be incredibly harsh, and the food generally tasteless, bland and overcooked. Nowhere served a decent spaghetti al dente with a simple, delicious tomato sauce like Mama's. These factors, combined with my intense working and study schedule, was completely wearing me out, as young as I was! When the time came for me to return to Sardinia, I was glad to do so.

At the end of my year of study, foreign students arrived for the summer English course, and I befriended a beautiful blonde girl, Jadranka, from Yugoslavia. We spent that summer together and, when we said our goodbyes at the airport, she made me promise to visit her back in her hometown. I returned home for the harvest, before being summoned for national service in the first week of January 1976.

At the beginning of November, I decided to make the trip and surprise Jadranka. She lived in Titograd, in Montenegro. I flew to Rome and connected with the only weekly service to Dubrovnik. I had chosen the worst possible day to travel – the flight was delayed due to bad weather. Soon after take-off, the JAT Yugoslav Airlines, Caravelle Jet aircraft began to sway strongly, struggling against the winds. When we reached the middle of the Adriatic Sea, the turbulence worsened.

Everyone tightened their seatbelts, gripping their armrests tightly; couples were holding hands nervously. As we approached the landing into Dubrovnik, with the plane wildly rising and falling, and the captain guiding the plane's course as best as he could, a sense of panic and hysteria took over some passengers. The flight attendants managed to quieten them down and, soon enough, with a quick jolt, the aircraft touched down on the tarmac, the engine going into reverse, announcing that we had landed safely. We all took a huge gasp of air, finally able to breathe normally again.

We had landed in the middle of an unseasonal winter snowstorm, with temperatures below zero. When I left Sardinia, temperatures had been well above 20 degrees, and this cold snap was unexpected. This was really a 'cold welcome' to the Socialist Federal Republic of Yugoslavia!

Dubrovnik airport was empty; summer had long ended. As I went through immigration, a red-starred officer looked at me as if I had come from Mars. I was certainly not equipped for the weather and must have seemed like I had arrived in the wrong month by mistake. Youngsters only visited in the heat of the summer, so he looked very puzzled as to what I was doing there!

In an empty arrivals hall, I approached the bus counter and asked for information on how to get to my destination. I was told to catch a bus to Herceg Novi and from there another bus would take me to Titograd. The journey to the coast town of Herceg Novi took about two hours, carrying just a handful of passengers on a rundown, outdated coach. I wrote my destination on a piece of paper to show the driver so that he would hopefully drop me off at the right stop for my next coach.

We arrived at Herceg Novi with an hour to spare and no waiting room; the surrounding buildings looked somewhat rundown and derelict. I sat down outside on a bench alone, and although the temperature had become slightly milder, I still felt very cold. A local middle-aged lady wrapped up a in fur coat, hat and scarf sat down beside me. I wondered why, as there were plenty of other empty benches. Then a man sat down next on the other side of me.

I started to feel uncomfortable as I was squeezed between them. The man pulled out a bottle of Slivovitz from his bag, took a big swig and offered me a sip from the bottle. I politely refused and he passed it on to the lady, who gladly accepted the offer. I stood up and pretended to pace in order to warm myself. Soon after, the man and woman huddled closer to each other, and a third person arrived and joined them. They were three perfect strangers, just trying keep warm on the winter day! Yet no one spoke a word.

At last, my coach pulled into the bus stop; it was a disconcertingly ancient vehicle for the four-hour trip to my destination. The two-lane road went via Budva, past beautiful views of lake-dotted countryside, then the road began winding through the hills until finally we drove into the town of Titograd, located on a wide, flat plain. I had at last arrived at my destination after the long day and it was getting dark. I took a short taxi ride to the Hotel Crna Gora, right at the centre of town. What a journey! I was finally able to relax in an incredibly old-fashioned but clean and warm room.

The following day I contacted Jadranka to surprise her, and immediately realized that I had made a big mistake. We met in the afternoon in a park not far from the hotel. She stood back and asked me to keep my distance, pretending we were strangers. She kept looking over her shoulder, looking rather uncomfortable and uneasy. Her behaviour felt unfamiliar to me and unnatural. Apparently, the secret police regularly spied on individuals, mostly on army officers and their families, her father was a colonel. She could be in serious trouble if she was caught with a foreigner. What followed were hours spent watching movies at the cinema in an alien language and chasing her around the park! Titograd did not offer very much in terms of entertainment or sightseeing during my week break. It turned out to have been one of those polite invites to visit with no real intentions behind it. The following Saturday morning, I boarded the 'Putnik' bus service to Dubrovnik airport. I felt extremely disenchanted with the disastrous visit and my departure heralded the end of our relationship.

As the 'Putnik', an OM Tigrotto bus, drove at a slow, steady pace on the steep and winding road, I reflected on what had just happened. Sardinia, being the 'Cinderella' of the Italian regions, had poverty, but the people I had seen here during my short stay were overwhelmingly poorer and seemingly forgotten. Babbu would be disappointed in the conclusions I reached about its political situation. He was sympathetic to socialist-communist regimes, believing that citizens were better off sharing resources among them equally. He certainly believed in a fair and just society.

Most evenings Babbu would listen to Radio Prague news, which was broadcast on longwave in Italian. He would sit in a half-lit corner of the kitchen after dinner at nine o'clock and tune in. We could always hear the soft whine of the broadcaster's voice fading in and out of aural clarity. He really needed to concentrate in order to understand. To me, Babbu looked like he was in a World War II movie: intriguing, mysterious, full of secrets.

When Bruno, my elder brother who had immigrated to Turin, applied for a job at Fiat, the car manufacturer, his application was immediately refused. They had received information from the authorities in Terralba, who had our father listed as a communist!

At the time, the Italian Communist Party was the second largest political party in the country. Babbu had perhaps voted for them, but he had never enrolled himself into any political parties and never attended or participated in any political events or protests. He warned us to do the same and stay out as this kind of activity, as it only stirred up trouble. On the town's cathedral door, there was a not so polite notice stating that communists were not welcome. This clearly never bothered him, as he always attended Sunday mass!

I had previously managed to defer my compulsory military service thanks to my studies but once I returned, I was required to fulfil my year of duties. I spent my first three months stationed in Cecchignola, a suburb of Rome, where I trained with one of the specialised army units.

Afterwards, I was transferred to Orvieto, a picturesque and historical Umbrian city, halfway between Rome and Florence. The city sits upon a summit of nearly vertical cliffs of volcanic rock. A funicular railway connects the city to the railway station, based downtown in the valley. The army barracks, which was built within the defensive wall of the city, was where new recruits trained before being transferred to their respective regiments.

The new recruits mostly originated from the southern regions of Italy, Sicily and Sardinia. It was a government policy that southerners were sent to the northern regions, and vice versa, so that the young men could assimilate the livelihoods and cultures of all fellow citizens of Italy. It was a harsh rule for some people, as some recruits hardly spoke any Italian and had never travelled outside of their villages before nor did they wish to do so. Illiteracy was high among Sicilians and Sardinians; they mingled with others only reluctantly, preferring to keep to themselves.

Initiation rituals were part of the military culture, and individuals were sometimes subjected to abusive treatment by the senior soldiers. Luckily, I had no such problems and must record that I was never bullied during my military service. Sardinians were characterized as bandits and introverts and were feared by all. I had also befriended a fellow Sardinian by helping him with some paperwork. He was a tough-looking shepherd who only spoke Sardo; I'm sure he was largely responsible for my trouble-free experience.

Together with a civilian employee, I was put in charge of

maintaining the electrics in the buildings. My duties were quite concise, and I tried to keep to myself most of the time. I visited my family in Terralba as much as I was permitted to do so.

One day I was summoned by the captain; he told me that he wanted to promote me to corporal! I politely refused; I was uninterested in any extra patrol duties. However, he was adamant, and assured me that I would be exempted of such duties, since he simply needed a corporal to inspect the daily cleaning duties of the dormitory. I was thus discharged in January 1977 with the rank of corporal.

Returning to Terralba, I took a temporary teaching job at the local secondary school while looking for other opportunities, and subsequently secured a permanent job teaching at the new technical college in Oristano, starting that September.

However, at the age of 23, being free from my compulsory civil duties, I wanted to fulfil my wanderlust by working abroad. I still had a strong desire burning inside me to discover the world, but I had no plans in place to reach my objective. Was it my destiny to become a teacher? Should I commit to the job, and could I be happy living a tranquil town life?

Chapter three

Seicelle

While at work one day, my elder brother, Gesuino, got news of a job vacancy for a technical assistant in an unheard of, faraway country. An archipelago in the middle of the ocean, he said. 'Is it in the Pacific?' I asked.

Gesuino could not be specific about the location but apparently, a local Sardinian entrepreneur had invested heavily in these islands. The news got me excited; I was both thrilled and puzzled. I wanted to know more.

The next day, Gesuino came back to tell me that role would be as an assistant to the managing director of a construction company based in the Seicelle. The candidate needed to have technical skills and knowledge, be trustworthy, dependable and relatively fluent in English; all my qualities, I reminded myself. This was the job for me!

The following day, by sheer coincidence, the mysterious entrepreneur turned up at Gesuino's office on business. Seizing the moment, Gesuino had a private word with him about me and my ambitions. The entrepreneur was very responsive to my qualifications and life story thus far. He was to leave the country in a few days, so he promptly set up an interview to meet me the following morning at his farm residence, an offer Gesuino thankfully accepted on my behalf.

In a short time, this strange encounter had brought me one step closer to fulfilling my dreams of travelling the world. I was ecstatic, and extremely excited about the forthcoming meeting. It was an opportunity to work and live abroad. I could not contain my feelings of joy, jumping in and out of the house and into the garden. 'Hold on, calm down, you are just going to a meeting! You are not leaving the country yet,' my Mama shouted loudly after me.

I had no clue yet of the whereabouts of the destination, Seicelle. I had never heard of these islands, even though I was rather good at geography at school! I knew of Centocelle, a historical district of Rome, which literally translates to 'one hundred cells' and therefore thought that Seicelle must translate into 'six cells'. I found such a name bizarre and funny for a country.

As the meeting was scheduled for the following morning, I spent all evening looking through my atlas and geography books in search of an archipelago named Seicelle. After many hours searching, I came across an old textbook with just four sentences describing the one hundred islands sprawled across the Indian Ocean between Madagascar and India, a tiny little dot in the World Atlas. A British colony, some remote tropical islands in the middle of nowhere! 'The Seychelles' was the English name of the archipelago. I also found a black and white picture of some kids jumping into the sea at the old pier in Victoria. Could this be my dream destination?

I dreamed all night of white sandy beaches fringed with coconut palm trees, pristine, clear waters and shallow lagoons filled with vivid coral reefs and multi-coloured fish. My mind reproduced and projected the images I had captured from looking at my magazines and books related to the South Pacific islands. These were the only tropical islands that were portrayed in films and talked about as holiday destinations for the ultra-rich.

I woke up early the next morning. The aroma of my mum's Lavazza mocha coffee was more intense and appealing than usual; the scent reached my bedroom, followed closely by the freshly made sponge cake she had baked for breakfast. I had a cool shower and shaved.

First impression count, I had been told. Trying to look smart, I dressed up in my best summer shirt. I stared at myself in the mirror and then changed shirts several times; finally, I picked the one that best matched my mood. My mum approved, 'You look ever so handsome,' she said in her firm and reassuring voice.

Chapter four

The Entrepreneur's Residence

It was early May 1977 and the Sardinian summer had begun in earnest. The weather was already hot and dry, and the days were getting longer and sunnier with incredibly clear blue skies. Temperatures were already in the late 20s by nine in the morning, boosted by the *scirocco*, the southern wind that blows in from the Sahara during the summer season. The wind, or *bentu asobi* in Sardinian, which means 'sun wind', gets hotter and hotter as it travels inland, reflecting from the surface crust of the Campidano plain.

My morning appointment was at the entrepreneur's residence some 45 minutes away from Terralba. As I backed my brand-new blue Citroen Dyane, purchased in cash from my summer jobs, out of the garage, Mama came out to wish me good luck, giving me a kiss on the cheek through the car window.

I drove past the main town square and took the road travelling north along the lagoons of Arborea, across the town of Oristano, and through ancient villages into the Sinis peninsula on the central west coast. The open countryside was a rural area of alternating flat farmland and rolling hills, lined with vineyards and fields of grain and rice. I had my windows open, as my Dyane had no air conditioning and, as the hot morning breeze blew in, I imagined what it would be like to live in the tropics – year-round summer weather of blue skies and beautiful beaches, I believed!

I had never been to this part of the island before and had to follow Gesuino's written instructions. Once I got closer, I had to leave the tarmac road to follow a dirt track for about 500 meters. *Unmissable, a long white painted boundary wall by the track,* Gesuino had written. I had reached my destination. The iron gate was already open; I was expected.

On each side of the entrance, there were rows of tall oleander trees, in shades of pink. I drove slowly, admiring the manicured gardens, the blooming colours of scarlet geraniums and other flowering beds. I thought of my mum, and how delighted she would be to see this place. Nestled between giant maritime pines and a grove of citrus trees, there was a beautiful Campidanese farmhouse villa, complete with a turret and bell tower.

It was an overwhelming sight; the property felt like an oasis. The morning heat was abated by the shade from the trees and the freshly irrigated gardens, and the air was filled with intense scents of rosemary, salvia and myrtle, which were growing at the garden's edges, a true Mediterranean aroma. I looked around and decided to park my car next to a dark blue Alfa Romeo Giulia. The matt-white villa had the iron window bars painted black. The isolated grounds were fenced in by high walls painted white, and finished off with red roof tiles. I noticed a security man standing by, dutifully guarding the property.

I turned off the car engine and checked my watch. I was early for the meeting, with ten minutes to spare. I composed myself, got out of the car and was looking at the villa's main entrance when a woman appeared out of the door and started to walk towards me. With a bright, smiling face, she introduced herself, '*Buongiorno*, I am Maria, the maid.' She was dressed in a gown that covered her knees with a white, embroidered-collar blouse. She was clearly Sardinian, tanned and of small stature. She looked unpretentious and had a friendly face.

She invited me in and said that Signor Cossu was expecting me. I thanked her and introduced myself, exchanging a few pleasantries in Sardinian, which made her laugh. She could not believe I was local because of my looks and height; I was tall compared to the average Sardinian.

We went through the entrance hall into the main lounge. The villa was furnished with antique wood furniture and the white walls were decorated with Sardinian art and tasteful ornaments. The floors were covered in red *cotto* tiles that shone as though they had just been freshly waxed. The ceiling was covered with a local bamboo-like cane, which reminded me of my grandad's house; it was an ancient way to insulate houses from the summer heat.

I was totally stunned by the beauty of the house. The entrance to the lounge had an archway, and I could not fail to notice a bronze church bell hanging in the centre with the dated inscription of 1864. Opposite this was a huge stone fireplace. The walls were ornate, hung with handmade Sardinian tapestries and artefacts representing various traditional cultures of the ancient civilisation that had once inhabited this remote part of the island.

The room was astonishingly bright due to a large, open glass door that spanned the entire wall. Flowering beds and dwarf palm trees surrounded the lawn, and a path led to a large swimming pool lined with sunbeds and parasols. The sitting area was divided by easy-chairs and sofas grouped in u-shapes and local handmade carpets laid out on the floor, delicately embroidered with Sardinian designs.

The property was part of a dairy farm, the *Azienda Agricola*, one of the largest in the region, with a substantial herd of cows and over 200 acres of agricultural land. The farm also had stables, a tennis court and even a private airstrip at the edge of the property.

I had no clue what to expect. Was I worried? That would be an understatement, but I tried to hold myself up. I had not met the man before and had little idea who he was. All I knew was that he could be the man who could change the path of my future.

Chapter five

The Governor

As I stood admiring the room, a middle-aged man entered from a separate hallway entrance. He was what I considered to be a typical Sardinian: medium height with tanned, olive skin and a stocky build. He was well-groomed with a fresh haircut and trimmed moustache. As he entered the room, he welcomed me and introduced himself as Corrado Cossu.

His smile was witty, *scherzoso,* and he complimented me saying I was 'a handsome young man.' He joked about my height, as Sardinians are notoriously small and I was almost two meters tall and skinny too! Perhaps he saw I was tense because he cracked a joke to break the ice. He thus made me feel relaxed and comfortable. Signor Cossu appeared to be a jolly, pleasant man.

He sat on an armchair, while I sat across from him on the sofa and we began exchanging questions and answers. At the time, I knew nothing about this man but later found out that he had quite the reputation. He was known for his eccentric personality, and was a well-educated, well-travelled man with many fascinating tales. Locally, he was known as '*Corradino*', little Corrado, but smart and sharp, *un dritto!* A truly legendary figure, people were captivated by his stories of adventure, which were often narrated in local bars, restaurants and businesses. Whether his tales were true, pure fantasies or just exaggerated, frankly did not matter as every Tom, Dick and Harry wanted to listen to them and share his anecdotes with others.

Signor Cossu's family wealth originated from his wife's inheritance. Signora Livia, known as Lily, was the daughter of a local landlord of noble origins dating back to the period when Spain ruled Sardinia in the 1700s. They had no children.

Signor Cossu had trained as an officer in the Carabinieri forces but in the late 1950s he had decided to retire for a more adventurous life. They had longed for a change of pace and they both had had a desire to explore the other side of the world, so they bought a large cattle ranch in the Rift Valley in Kenya, modelling themselves on the British colonial lifestyle, as seen in the characters of the film *Out of Africa*. They had loved the pampered life, where there were servants around to attend to their need. It was while living in Kenya that they visited the Seychelles, a British colony, for the first time.

Long before the airport was built, the only way to reach this remote archipelago was by sea. The twin ocean liners *Kampala* and *Karanja,* owned by the British India Steam Navigation Company, linked East Africa and India. The liners sailed from Mombasa to Bombay every month with a stopover in Port Victoria; in total, the journey was three days long. The arrival and departure of the steam liner in Victoria produced quite a gathering of curious crowds every time. The Cossu's stay in the Seychelles had been memorable; they loved the islands and, being islanders themselves, they felt a familiarity in the place. They vowed to return on holiday.

The Mau-Mau Uprising of 1952-60, which sparked Kenya's move to independence, abruptly brought an end to their life there. Though their farm was burned and destroyed by the rebels, they managed to escape and survived the tragedy, finding refuge with family friends in Nairobi.

Undeterred by these tumultuous events, they decided without hesitation to move permanently to the Seychelles. At the time, the islands were untouched by tourism because of their remoteness. However, their isolation from the rest of the world was soon to change, as the project of the Seychelles International Airport, financed by the British Government, was already in the advanced stages. Signor Cossu was certain that, once the airport was built and running, tourists would come in droves to visit these beautiful islands.

The country of Seychelles offered a vast number of prospects for investment by entrepreneurs in all sectors of the economy. Signor Cossu seized the opportunity and established a full range of business ventures. These included ventures in real estate, construction and property development, the hotel to the restaurant trade, the import and export of commerce, and travel and the airline business. He was soon running a rather large network of organisations.

Sure enough, the international airport opened in 1971, with East African Airways operating flights from Nairobi, closely followed by the British Overseas Airline Company with a weekly flight from London on a Super VC10 aircraft. The Seychelles were no longer isolated. With their doors open to the world, tourists flocked in, just as Cossu had predicted. He had revealed himself to be a remarkable and adaptable businessman.

He was appointed Honorary Consul for Italy; this official status gave him recognition and further standing within the governmental ranks and diplomatic corps of the country. He had also established good relations with politicians and civil servants, a means to keep everyone at arm's length. Although charming and well spoken, he was also a shrewd and astute communicator. He kept talking and telling me about his intrepid life.

The airstrip on his estate intrigued me. Cossu explained that he had got his pilot licence in Kenya to facilitate his travels between Nairobi and his remote farm in the Rift Valley. He had managed to fly the Piper Navajo aircraft from Kenya to Seychelles via the Comoros Islands and Diego Suarez in Madagascar, a journey that had taken more than ten hours. Once in Mahé, he had continued flying it as an air-taxi service between airfields.

This had inspired him to fly from Mahé to Sardinia. In October 1973, he set out on his journey to Kenya, on to North Africa and finally to the Mediterranean. The African coastline stretches for more than a thousand miles across the Indian Ocean. To make the trip, Cossu had had to modify the Piper Navajo tanks to carry more fuel. It took him and his co-pilot just over five hours to complete the journey to Mombasa. He said he encountered many obstacles along the route, but the scariest moments were cruising 20,000 feet above the Egyptian airspace. Two MiG-21 Egyptian Air Force fighter planes appeared and forced him to land. Unbeknownst to him, he had been flying in a restricted military area and failed to respond to traffic control. They ended up in jail! But luckily, once they established their identities, they were cleared for release. As an apology for this imprisonment, the Egyptian authorities gave him and his co-pilot a reception of the kind he had never seen before. For a few days, they were offered the kind of hospitality not seen since the time of the pharaohs! He later reached his destination and landed at his airstrip in Sardinia. A few weeks later, with his mission accomplished, he sold the aircraft to the Aero Club in Cagliari. He described the whole journey as a purely exhilarating experience.

I was captivated by the way he described this trip; I could have listened to him for hours. He reminded me of a schoolteacher I had had earlier in the detailed way he described events, and he quickly earned my admiration.

Signor Cossu was aiming to expand his business ventures on a scale never before seen on the no-longer remote archipelago of the Seychelles. To achieve this project, he needed qualified and experienced managers and administrative staff to oversee the day-to-day operations.

The purpose of my visit was to be interviewed for the job, but Signor Cossu kept talking non-stop. Suddenly, perhaps realising the time, he interrupted his life-story monologue. He was short and sweet when he said that I had come highly recommended and that he was more than delighted to make my acquaintance. He asked me to visit him in the Seychelles and, if I liked the place, join his management team. He would employ me in the role of personal assistant to Mr Floris, the Managing Director of his construction company, SOGIS.

He said he would make all the travel arrangements and, once the paperwork was in order, he would mail me the airline tickets for the journey. As I sat there with him, I tried to contain my feelings. I felt so happy. I was going to the Seicelle. Signor Cossu described it to me as an 'earthly paradise,' and the 'Garden of Eden.'

I left his villa shortly before lunchtime. I could not wait to share the news with Gesuino and my parents. I drove home, mindlessly daydreaming about the opportunity. Mama was thrilled for me; she knew how much I wanted it. In her life, she had never got the chance to go anywhere, and she loved the idea that one day I would relate my travels to her. However, Babbu found it hard to accept my desire to go abroad in search of new opportunities. Life according to him was confined to his courtyard. When Gesuino came back from work later that evening, we celebrated with few bottles of Ichnusa beer. He was so pleased for me. The next day, I made a list of things I needed for the journey. Passport, vaccination jabs, summer clothes, first-aid kit; Mama even suggested packing some *spaghetti*. Surely a good idea!

Chapter six

Planning My Trip

Some three weeks after my pleasant meeting with Signor Cossu, news arrived from the Seychelles: there had been a change of government. The reports spoke about *un colpo di stato* – the opposition leader had staged a coup d'état, overthrowing the elected president while he was abroad. However, the news was incomplete and disjointed and did not provide enough information.

Gradually, as more news slowly trickled through, it became clear the event had taken place a few days before, on 5 June. The prime minister had removed the president from office in what was described as a 'bloodless coup'. Learning of this was devastating as my trip planning came grinding to a halt at once.

I had no idea what this meant for the future of Signor Cossu's business. Would this change the nature of his investments? I felt inert, stunted. I had no choice but to wait for further news and instructions. Gesuino kept in touch with his contacts in Oristano, but receiving information from the islands was very precarious as the only means of communication was through an unreliable telephone line. Italian newspapers and radio did not report the news of the coup in Seychelles – perhaps the media did not know even of the existence of the country. Mind you, I had only just found out about the archipelago few weeks earlier myself!

Not only did my trip planning stop, but I also began to doubt the whole affair. Was it safe to travel to such a remote and unknown destination, a banana republic?

Perhaps it was all a farce of bad taste and Babbu was right after all. This was an extraordinary situation for me. Would it end in a fiasco, just another one of Signor Cossu's long list of stories? I had lots to think about while I waited!

I decided to proceed with having my jabs, as the yellow fever vaccine was taken in two doses, a month apart, which involved travelling to Cagliari each time. I prepared my passport too. In between, I tried to distract myself by enjoying the good weather, going to the beach with friends.

Summer went by, and it was not until later in September that I learned my trip was still on. After months of waiting, my airline ticket arrived by post. It was an awfully expensive open return ticket; as per our accord, I could return at any time if conditions were not to my liking. I had no employment contract, no terms and conditions drawn, nor had I even discussed my arrangements, for that matter. A blind date had been set up with these enigmatic, minute tropical islands out in the middle of the Indian Ocean.

Chapter seven

The Outbound Journey

Gesuino drove me to the airport; my mum insisted on coming along to say her goodbyes. She was anxious and protective of all her sons but, since I was the youngest, she had established a special bond with me. When realised that I would be gone soon, she found it hard to let me go.

As the plane took off from Cagliari airport, I felt like a bird venturing out of its golden cage for the first time. I felt a multitude of emotions, apprehensive to be flying into the unknown, to an unfamiliar and now troubled exotic place. But what I wanted and dreamed of was finally happening. I was ecstatic yet sad to have left my family in tears.

The flight took me to Rome. From there, I flew to Cairo, Addis Ababa and Mogadishu on an old but freshly painted Somali Airlines Boeing 720. The flight had originated in Frankfurt, and from Rome to Mogadishu with the stop-over in between it was a busy, full flight.

At the front of the aircraft was a first-class cabin with a smoking section in the front rows, followed by the economy non-smoking section at the rear of the plane. I sat in one of the non-smoking seats towards the back, which turned out to be an ideal position from which to observe the passengers and crew activities throughout the flight.

All hand luggage was stored in a net above the seats that was built along both sides of the plane. The bulging net would annoy some passengers when they stood up. When we stopped in Cairo, the cabin was filled with the unfamiliar and exotic scents of the new passengers, the combination of leather accessories and body perspiration, I assumed. When we hit turbulence, some of the metal artefacts being carried by the Egyptian passengers clashed against each other.

With the aircraft full of passengers from all ethnic backgrounds, it seemed to me like a difficult bunch to deal with, but the tall, beautiful Somali hostesses tended to each person's needs, graciously serving food and drinks. They also had the troublesome task of plugging the leaks from the ceiling along the aisle, which were due to the defective air-conditioning insulation system. The quick tissue-paper fix was not effective nor an appealing sight, as they hung like small stalactites in a cave roof!

I did not know that the wife of my future boss, Mr Floris, was also on the same flight, accompanied by their two daughters. We introduced ourselves just before departing from Rome and then sat apart on the plane. Being a smoker, she had taken smoking seats in the front cabin.

On the last leg of our journey, we were joined by a Seychelles minister of agriculture and land use by the name of Dr Maxime Ferrari. He was apparently a particularly good friend of Signor Cossu and was returning home after one of his ministerial visits to an unnamed country. Signora Floris had met him before and, as the minister settled in his first-class seat, they exchanged a short conversation. The Mogadishu-Seychelles route was not a busy flight, so there were lots of empty seats about, giving me an opportunity to stretch out and relax.

As we flew across the Indian Ocean, the flight got bumpier, but we were reassured that it was a common occurrence – crosswinds meeting over the open seas. We had the seat belts on for most of the two-and-a-half-hour flight. As we approached our final destination, the captain announced our descent. The morning light had just broken and white-grey clouds crowned the blue sky. From my window, I spotted a group of islands with hilly tops, surrounded by vividly coloured seas.

We flew over what seemed to be the capital, Victoria, approaching the runway north of the airport on the main island of Mahé. As we continued to descend, the views became clearer. To my right were mountains covered by lush tropical greenery and on my left were small islands surrounded by white beaches, lush vegetation and an emerald, green sea. The runway, built on reclaimed land in between islands, appeared suddenly as the aircraft tyres hit the tarmac and the engine eased off its power. We had landed. The entire journey had taken more than 24 hours, but the overwhelming beauty of the place suppressed my exhaustion.

Chapter eight

The Seychelles

One thousand miles from the East African coastline, scattered across the Indian Ocean between Madagascar and India, is the archipelago of Seychelles, some 115 tropical islands primarily made up of granite. It is believed these islands were once part of the supercontinent Gondwana, which gradually broke apart millions of years ago. During the separation, chunks of land split into small parts and these fragments became islands.

The Seychelles were unclaimed virgin lands until the early 1700s, when they were used as a refuge for pirates and buccaneers who raided the merchant's ships trading across these uncharted waters, and a safe haven in which to shelter from storms. The islands also provided a transit point for Arab slave traders, moving people along the lengthy, perilous journey from the East African coast to the Saudi Arabia peninsula.

They were uninhabited until 1770, when the French took possession and established a colony on the island of Sainte Anne, across from today's capital of Victoria, with fifteen white men, eight African slaves and five Indian servants.

The French handed the islands to the British in 1814 under the Treaty of Paris, following the defeat of Napoleon at Waterloo. However, it was not until 1903 that the archipelago officially became a British Crown Colony. Because of its remoteness, the colony turned out to be a suitable place in which to exile political detainees and troublemakers who were against the British Empire's governance. From the late 1800s to the middle of the 20th century, the Malaysian Sultan of Perak, the Ghanaian King of Ashanti, two kings of Buganda (Uganda) and Archbishop Makarios of Cyprus were imprisoned there, to name a few.

The islands were neglected and starved of any investment for decades. It was not until 1964 that local political parties were formed, who began campaigning for better standards of living and self-government.

The Seychelles played a strategic role in the international field from the early 1970s, when its location was highlighted once again, but this time as a possible naval airbase. Just along the equator and in close proximity to the vital oil-shipping route at the crossroads between the Suez Canal and Cape of Good Hope, the islands became a bone of contention between world powers, who have tried to assert their political influence ever since. The USA and the USSR even outplayed each other during their 'friendly rivalry' in the Cold War. The USA built a satellite tracking station on the main island of Mahé in 1963, paying an annual rent of nearly $3 million, a key forex earner for the country.

In 1974, both major political parties campaigned for independence, and the wind of change arrived in the Seychelles on 29 June 1976, with the creation of an independent republic.

The first two major parties agreed to share power in the newborn nation. The leader of the Seychelles Democratic Party, James Mancham, was elected president and the opposition leader of the Seychelles People's United Party, Albert René was handed the position of prime minister.

President Mancham was the son of a Chinese merchant who had been educated in England: a flamboyant character, a playboy and *joie de vivre* symbol of the Seychelles. Mancham was associated with Adnan Khashoggi, the millionaire Arab arms dealer. Together, they wanted to turn Seychelles into the Monte Carlo of the Indian Ocean.

Not even a year had passed when Prime Minister France Albert

René, a socialist Sino-Russian sympathizer, overthrew Mancham in a 'bloodless' coup d'état on 5 June 1977, with support from the Tanzanian President Nyerere, Cuban leader Fidel Castro and Kim II-Sung of North Korea. This was the coup that had occurred during the year of my arrival. René saw these pro-Soviet countries as models for his own country to follow. He turned the country into a one-party state, tightening his grip on security forces and neutering the opposition. He curtailed the press and exerted control of the judiciary branch. René embraced the socialist ideology and applied its principles to this tropical paradise.

Before the coup, Seychelles had no armed forces, and law and order was regulated by the police force, which had been trained by British police officers. The Seychelles Police had insignificant armoury and followed similar practices and rules to the British police. After the coup, René created a military force of more than 8,000 soldiers; over 10% of the entire population was employed in the new created army. The Tanzanian forces stationed there trained the soldiers, and a chain of command was created. Albert René was the commander-in-chief and Berlouis, as minister of defence, became second in command.

René was a strong, resolute leader, but he was self-obsessed and saw enemies everywhere, mistrusting his own cabinet of ministers and the military command. His own bodyguard unit was made up of North Korean soldiers stationed by the State House, a benevolent gift from President Il-Sung during René's state visit to North Korea, as a marker of his support.

Initially, René reassured citizens and foreign investors of his good intentions. His newly appointed ministers were sent abroad to appease international governments, arguing that they were working for the good of the nation.

Chapter nine

Landing in Mahé

It was Sunday morning in Mahé. The health authorities were busying themselves with necessary checks before allowing us to disembark. Upon landing, the Somali air hostesses disinfected the aircraft against the spread of malaria, as Seychelles is a malaria-free country. I sat impatiently, eager to get off the plane and begin my adventure. I pinched myself on the arm, just to make sure that I was awake!

Once outside the air-conditioned cabin, I was hit by a light breeze of hot and humid tropical air. My body began to sweat instantly, my shirt sticking to my skin. I felt like a different person; nothing else mattered now but my new life on these islands. Everything looked magical, as far my eyes could see.

I entered the small terminal, where listless ceiling fans were blowing the humid air around. I had to take in a few deep breaths and pause for a short moment. The combination of heat and exhaustion had made me dizzy.

I recovered and moved quickly through immigration formalities. An officer in a dark blue uniform asked me the reason for my trip. 'Holidays,' I replied, as instructed by Signor Cossu. I produced my return flight ticket. He enquired where I would be staying and for how long. His part of the short conversation was impartial and expressionless. Satisfied with my answers, he stamped the immigration card and my passport, handing them back to me together with my flight ticket. I collected my suitcase and queued for customs. The customs officer, dressed smartly in a white uniform, checked my luggage for prohibited items. She made me open my hand luggage and asked me a few more questions. Once she was satisfied, I was in the clear.

I exited the security area to find Signor Cossu and Mr Floris waiting there to greet me and also welcome his own family back. We were briefly introduced and then, understandably, Mr Floris wanted to take the family home to rest, so they swiftly jumped into their vehicles and left.

A taxi was to take me to accommodation at the Pirates Arms Hotel in Victoria. My driver, a middle-aged man with an afro and dark glasses, drove his patched-up Peugeot station wagon without haste or hurry to pick up another fare. We drove lazily along the beautiful winding and bumping coastline road, passing unusual tropical plants and bushes. Small clusters of colourfully painted houses were scattered along the road, obstructing the sea view. To make conversation, the driver asked me about my trip in broken English with a strong local accent. I happily replied to all his enquiries, but I was now feeling tired from the journey. Although it was morning, I could not wait to get to bed and rest.

We arrived at the Pirates Arms, only to be told that the hotel was fully booked. But they had reserved another room at a nearby guest house, The Harbour View at Monte Fleuri. Luckily, when I arrived, my bedroom was ready, and I dropped my bags to the floor, exhausted. The room was simply furnished. It had no air conditioning, just a floor fan that blew hot, stuffy air around the room. I locked the door, took off my sweaty clothes and hopped in the shower. It had no cubicle, just a frail curtain hanging to contain the spraying water. After cooling off, I dried myself with a towel and immediately felt the sweat creep back under my armpits. The air in the room was steamy and sticky. I opened the louvered glass windows to let wind in and laid down on the bed naked, falling instantly into a deep sleep.

Suddenly, I could feel myself being teased into consciousness by a peculiar tickling, up and down, all over my naked body. My eyes flicked open and re-adjusted to the dark. Some large, honey-brown insects had flown in. They were cockroaches, crawling all over me! I jumped up, swatting them off me. Feeling agitated, I fled to the shower to rinse myself off and remove them all. Disgusted by the unpleasant encounter, I made my way to the reception desk with only a towel around my waist. I was furious, but the woman on duty, ignoring my complaints, calmly pulled out a red can from underneath the desk, walked into my room and sprayed the aerosol around liberally. 'There', she said, 'that will do, and keep the louvers closed.' These crawling creatures had wrecked my first night in 'paradise.'

I woke up to what was to be the first day of my new adventure: life in the Seychelles. I heard the church bells toll twice, announcing the six o'clock dawn, and the room filled with light – as if someone had switched the electric lights on. I stretched my bones, wrapping the bedsheet around me. Looking around the room, I saw that the cockroaches from the night before were belly-up dead. I raised myself from the bed and opened the curtain to look through the window, realising that my room at the guesthouse was at the edge of a mangrove swamp. It was low tide and the water had receded to expose the seabed. White heron, *madanm paton*, were about in search of fish and crabs. Black birds with yellow beaks, *marten*, and large seagulls made a racket. I opened the window louvers to catch the fresh breeze. Without realising it, I started singing. Merrily, I went for a shower and dressed in a fresh, new t-shirt taken from the top of my unpacked suitcase.

Breakfasting on the patio on homemade cinnamon cake and local tea, I pored over a tourist information guide that I had been handed at the airport. It made an interesting read, a quick way to familiarise a visitor with local dos and don'ts. Nature had been kind to the islands; there were no fatally poisonous animals living in the Seychelles. However, the guide warned that the coral reefs had dangerous, venomous stonefish that people often stepped on accidentally, along with fire coral, which was easily mistaken for seaweed. On contact with human skin, the coral could cause intense pain for days and even leave scarring. The guide suggested observing the reefs from afar without touching the structure. For me, any such information was valuable.

Chapter ten

Yellow Mini Moke

The company driver picked me up to move me into a three-bedroom house at Glacis, in the north of Mahé. It was a Monday morning and Victoria seemed lively as the shops were already opening for the day's trading. The driver was taciturn and spoke only a few words of English. He drove us straight to my new home almost entirely in silence, in contrast to the bustling sounds of life around me.

The company rented the house I would be sharing with Nicola, known as Nick, an Italian structural surveyor who also worked with them. He only sporadically stayed at the house, as he was in charge of the Praslin Island project and when in Mahé he preferred to spend the nights at his Seychellois girlfriend's house.

Two days later I was given a yellow Mini Moke as my means of transport. I was delighted; the little car had no doors or windows, just a chassis with four wheels, a front engine and a black fabric canopy top. Fired-up with the excitement of having my very own vehicle with which to explore the island, I embarked on my first drive. The car was orientated to drive on the left-hand side of the road, which was new to me. Travelling along the winding road, the lanes were quite empty. I was instantly reminded of my Lambretta at home, with the wind in my hair giving me the same carefree sensation.

I had left some papers for the office on the passenger seat, as the Moke did not have a glove box. Taking a bend, the wind caught the papers. I instinctively reached out to save them from flying out of the car, simultaneously steering the Moke off the road and crashing into the sea at Anse Etoile. Thankfully, it was low tide, and, apart from a minor injury, I got off scot-free. My little Moke, however, was beached! Some local residents came to my aid, getting me out of the car and into the yard of a house. While they attended to my forehead injury, a group of men got together and lifted the car effortlessly from the sea. They rescued it before the tide came in and secured my car on dry land. What an amazing gesture of kindness; I was impressed!

I learned later that the Moke's steering had been compromised following a previous accident and that, because original spares were unavailable and second-hand spares hard to find, it had been repaired by mechanics who had improvised with whatever parts they could get their hands on. Improvisation and adaptation played a significant role in island life.

Cargo ship supplies only arrived once a month and often goods and provisions were not to be found until the next shipment. At times, even essential goods were scarce; this was also the land of *napa*, of 'none', the Seychellois would say.

I was smitten with the beauty of the country: the scenery, the warm turquoise water and pristine beaches, the friendly people with their carefree approach to life, and the tropical weather. Just after a few days after arriving, I could not wish for a better place to be – minus the cockroaches and the car accident! I started to gather my bearings as I settled into my new house, feeling happy about it all.

Chapter eleven

The Drive into Victoria

A few days later, I took a leisurely drive into town via Beau Vallon beach, as I was only expected later in the morning. The winding road took me from my house at Glacis along the coastline, past all the tropical vegetation of coconut trees and flowers of all varieties: bursts of sunshine yellow and fire-tree red. The huge, green breadfruit trees, with their unique leaf shapes and cantaloupe-sized fruit, were mixed up in between huge granite boulders.

I recognised the pink flowers as wild bougainvillea and the orange and yellow lantanas, which matched the plants in Mama's garden in Terralba. To my left, the view of the ocean kept changing as I drove along, like stills on a television screen.

Upon reaching the stunning beach at Beau Vallon, I stopped, parked the car between two huge takamaka trees at the edge of the sandy beach and admired the incredible view. The sun reflected on the calm waters and the imposing granitic island of Silhouette, shrouded in cloud, could be seen in the distance. The beach was almost deserted except for local fishermen preparing for their catch of the day. The beach was still shaded by the takamaka and coconut trees because the sun rose from the east, but the sooty terns were already in full swing, catching breakfast for their chicks.

The ocean was calm but for a light breeze that tickled its surface. Suddenly, a swarm of glittering silver fins shone through the water, reflecting the morning sunshine. A shoal of mackerel rippled the serene water turning it choppy and crinkled.

The fishermen had gone out to sea in their pirogue, and I stood by the Moke watching the spectacle that was the Seychellois way of fishing. One team stayed on the beach, holding the end of the net. As the pirogue moved away from the shoreline, one of the three men on board was rowing, one was steering, and the third swung the net into the water. It seemed all very precisely coordinated and routinely performed.

The pirogue went out to sea and then re-routed to run parallel to the shore, forming a half-moon tour around the bay. With their net in the water, they returned to the shoreline and heaved the pirogue onto the beach. Grasping the end of the rope, the men started pulling the net in at each end. Slowly and in sequence, the men pulled the rope, alternating their grip. The pulling became harder as the number of fish caught in the net became heavier. Thousands of mackerels were caught and dragged forcefully ashore. It was unbelievable; I had never seen anything remotely like it.

A small crowd of people gathered to help the fishermen collect the catch. Three or four mackerel were tied together by passing a string through the fish gills and mouth. The tied-up fish were then ready to be sold by the roadside to passers-by or delivered to the Victoria fish market.

I suddenly realised that I had been there for over an hour; it was time for me to carry on with my driving. The road continued uphill to the peak at St Louis, where I admired the breath-taking views of Victoria and the inner islands.

Entering Victoria, I negotiated my way through tightly compacted buildings grouped next to one another, and picturesque old-style shops that merged with newly constructed offices. The vibrantly coloured grocery and souvenir shop fronts and shutters were in stark contrast to the sterile beige or white façades of the newer dwellings. The diverse flavours and cultures of the merchants, and the fact that the open market was still in its old colonial setting collided to create a small but thriving commercial centre. As I turned round onto the main street, a sizeable Catholic missionary house appeared on my left, prominently raised up from road level, followed by the cathedral with a bell tower at the back. I remember the peculiarity of the clock striking twice every hour.

The shops had names like Chaka Bros, Sham Peng Tong, Oliajee, Adam Moosa, Kim Koon, and Valabhji, and my nose picked up the scent of spicy herbs and aromas emanating from their premises. The road brought me to the main roundabout, which featured a silver-coloured replica of the Vauxhall Bridge clock tower in London. This was the very centre of Victoria, intercepting the State House Avenue and Independence Avenue. All the cogs of the Seychelles government machine were now within a short range: the State House, now the President's office; Liberty House, home of the Ministry of Finance and the Treasury; the Post Office, the courthouse, and the banks.

I noticed that Victoria had exceptionally clean roads. The flowerbeds were maintained by convicts dressed in light blue uniforms, transported daily by boat from Long Island, a designated prison from colonial times. Seychellois men and women walked calmly and unhurriedly along the pavements, some with shopping bags made from palm leaves, others carrying babies and open umbrellas to shade themselves from the blazing sunshine. The odd white businessperson could be seen hurrying to their office. It was too early for tourists to be about.

A flavour of pre-independence elitist life was still in the air. Landowners, referred to as *gran blan*, literally meaning 'big white', and the 'governing elite' all had special privileges. Most of the population were illiterate with no formal education and spoke Creole, a French patois with a heavy East African and Malagasy influence. The official languages in Seychelles were English, followed by French, a legacy of their first colonisers. Life looked so peaceful and simple, and I found the Creole people to be quite similar to the old folks in Terralba who would stand up at the sight of anyone dressed well enough to convey a look of authority, removing their hats as a sign of respect.

I drove slowly, as the roads were not busy, and kept glancing around me, savouring the experience of my first drive into town. Turning left at the clock tower roundabout, I drove onto Independence Avenue, parking behind Kingsgate House. I had arrived, fresh and confident, ready to meet my dragons.

Chapter twelve

The Company's Office

Signor Cossu had arranged for us to meet at the company's office building so I could be introduced to the team. The top man was Mr Perrillo, Group General Manager of Cossu's companies. He was well-educated and Italian-English, fluent in both languages. He had an abundance of experience, having worked in Zambia with Alitalia as station manager at Lusaka airport, and for a large Italian engineering company in Arusha, Tanzania. The two had met in Tanzania and, after Signor Cossu had spent a lot of time cajoling him, terms were agreed and Perrillo decided to move to the Seychelles. He had a young family with two small children and an English wife.

Perrillo had a strong, resolute character; he seemed quite meticulous and discreet with his work. He also appeared to be a delightful chap, well-mannered and softly spoken. He was inspirational and, given the chance, I knew I could learn lots from him. I liked his English manner and the way he engaged in business. As I came to know him better, however, I realised that he was not fully prepared to share administrative tasks with me, and he kept my friendly eagerness to excel at bay.

Perrillo and Signor Cossu were inseparable. The only time Signor Cossu would be alone in his office was during his consular duties or while meeting private guests; Mr Perrillo would take on his consular role when Signor Cossu was overseas.

Mr Floris was to be my immediate boss; he was also Sardinian, a civil engineer by profession, and managing director of the construction company SOGIS. He had acquired SOGIS shares from Dr Maxime Ferrari.

Dr Maxime Ferrari, a medical doctor of Italian descent, had been a

Cossu family friend since his arrival in the Seychelles. Ferrari and Cossu had formed SOGIS together, turning it into a successful business. In 1974, longing for a political career, Ferrari decided to sell his equity shares in SOGIS to Mr Floris on Signor Cossu's recommendation so that he could pursue his ambitions. They remained good friends and Signor Cossu counted on him for fresh government policies and for his insights on current affairs. During the coup d'état, the good doctor had played a prominent role, supporting Albert René's cause. René rewarded him by appointing him as vice-president and minister of land use.

In his late fifties, Mr Floris reminded me of my father in many ways. He was well-organised, diligent, immensely proud, and enthusiastic about his professional role. He was also unsophisticated, unadventurous and provincial in character – a down-to-earth man who measured business risk in profound detail. He was incredibly careful with spending; his approach had little in common with the daring attitude of Signor Cossu. Floris had been relatively happy and content to live the rest of his life in the provincial town of his birth. Therefore, I wondered why he was in the Seychelles. What on earth had motivated him to be here? He had never been overseas before his Seychelles expedition and, moreover, had never imagined he would be working in such a tropical, exotic place at his age. I felt like I needed to understand his motives for being in the country.

Floris and Cossu were old friends who had attended the same school as teenagers, but in different classes. Later, they hung out occasionally with same circle of friends and associates. It was in the summer of 1974 that Signor Cossu enticed Mr and Mrs Floris to visit the Seychelles on holiday, during a dinner party at Floris's beach house. Signor Cossu offered to make all the travel arrangements and to host them at his villa in Mahé. They could not pass on such a generous offer. Going overseas to an exotic place was an extraordinary change to their usual summer holidays at a seaside villa, a 30-minute drive from their townhouse. Cossu was a famously remarkable host and during the Floris's stay in the Seychelles, he made everything look utterly alluring, showing them the untroubled pace of island life. They were captivated; they fell in love with the country and made plans for a future investment in Signor Cossu's enterprises. However, Mr Floris's business in Sardinia was a partnership with a fellow engineer, a Mr Cherchi, who did not trust Cossu's business intentions.

Mr Floris saw an opportunity to diversify their business in a country full of promise and he was willing to take the risk, convinced it would bring good rewards and professional satisfaction. He also loved the idea of working in a country where it was summer all year around!

Finally, a compromise was reached between Mr Floris and Mr Cherchi. The latter would take control of their Sardinian businesses and Mr Floris would manage their new affairs in the Seychelles.

With their two daughters still at university in Italy, Mrs Floris was to commute and visit as often as she could, coordinating her travel with her daughters' school terms. Perrillo and Floris were next-door neighbours, renting two bungalows at the exclusive Machabee Estate on the northeast point of Mahé.

While Mr Floris was in full charge of the construction company SOGIS, he spoke little English, and my job as personal assistant mainly consisted of translating for him during his daily work routine, meeting government officials and communicating to our foremen on site. SOGIS was remarkably busy, being involved in two large projects: the construction of Ocean Gate House in Victoria, nearing its completion stage when I arrived, and the construction of a tourist resort in Praslin, a nearby island, that was in its initial stages.

I discovered I was completely unqualified for the job. My responsibilities were daunting and I felt uncomfortable in the role, as I had no idea what I was supposed to be doing. I had to figure things out soon enough, though, because I had made up my mind; I was here to stay. I was going to accept the position that Signor Cossu had offered me. I had no reason to doubt myself; maybe I truly did not have the skills necessary for the job, but the combination of willingness to learn from my mentor and my capacity to adapt would see me through my tasks. I was eager to rise to the challenge, no matter what!

Chapter thirteen

Making New Friends

Nick, my housemate, was also part of the SOGIS managerial team; he was a qualified quantity surveyor, who was in charge of the SOGIS operation on the island of Praslin.

I had not met him since I had arrived, as he was away. On the morning of my visit to the office, he flew straight in from the airport and we met at the SOGIS office. Over a cup of local vanilla-infused tea we got to know each other a little more. Nick was a loud guy, fat and short in stature, from southern Italy. I came to discover that he always wore a long-sleeved shirt when at the office, and it seemed his body never adjusted to the tropical heat because he was always uncomfortably sweaty. He had previously worked in construction in Uganda. He spoke excellent English and was highly experienced at his job.

He was meeting with Mr Floris for a full report on the progress of operations and I was asked to attend, although informally. Nick showed me how to order and replenish the various building materials needed at the site. Transport of all goods, such as cement and timber, had to be done by sea and space had to be booked in advance. The *Praslinoise* was the only sailing schooner that travelled to and from Praslin daily. The vessel was relatively small, but it carried cargo and passengers if space was available.

Nick was a pleasant man; his presentation and clear instructions were easy to follow. He asked if I would like to join him for dinner at his girlfriend's house that evening, which I gladly accepted as an opportunity to make new friends.

We returned to the house after work, and, after a cool shower and a change of clothes, we drove down to his girlfriend's house in St Louis. I learned that the estate, which consisted of several dwellings, belonged to the Morel family. Madame Morel, a gracious old lady, lived in her own colonial house on the estate, just meters from Anne, Nick's girlfriend. Meanwhile, Mr Morel lived at his grocery shop just down across the road. Mr and Mrs Morel were also the parents of Guy Morel, the permanent secretary of the Ministry of Finance.

Anne was very welcoming and pleased to make my acquaintance. She cooked a good variety of Creole food – local smoked marlin with mango salad, a large grilled *bourgeois,* a red snapper, a delicious fish loaf, rice, salads and tasty banana cake. She prepared the food and displayed the lot on serving dishes, buffet-style, on her long dining table in one corner of the living room. Attending dinner was her young son, David, and Helena, her sister.

Helena was very beautiful. She was dressed in the tight-fitting uniform of a local travel agency. She had dark brown eyes and her skin was a creamy ivory. Anne also shared the same dark brown eyes but had curly thick hair and a rich south-Asian complexion; you had to study them closely to see they were sisters. Helena had a canny but sensual, shy smile. She was mostly chatty and in control of the conversation at the table and showed a self-confident character. I reckoned she was in her mid-twenties.

Their father, Monsieur Morel, was an elderly chap of French origin with distinctive blue eyes. Anne had inherited her creole features from their mother, Madame Morel.

Dinner went well; Anne had made sure the food was not too spicy for my benefit, under Nick's instructions. Away from the table, Helena remarked to Anne that I had lovely hands with beautiful long fingers. Anne reported her compliment to Nick, adding, "I bet these two will end up together." After dinner, I drove back to Glacis alone, as Nick had decided to spend the night at Anne's.

Chapter fourteen

Permit to Work

As I had entered the country on a tourist visa, so now I needed a permit to work. The law required that the job vacancy be advertised first in the local newspaper, as the Seychellois had priority to any jobs available. If no suitable candidates applied, then a foreign candidate with appropriate qualifications could be given a work permit to fulfil the post.

The Immigration Office was in the same building as our SOGIS office and arrangements were made for me to be interviewed and assessed. Signor Cossu called in favours in return for the fast processing of my application.

When I arrived to be interviewed, I was introduced to the chief immigration officer, Gerald Hoarau. He welcomed me into his office and, to my surprise, started speaking Italian. He was fluent, with a good accent. He had attended a seminary in Rome, studying for the priesthood until his desire for the vocation had died out and he returned to the Seychelles. He had studied Latin, Italian and theology there.

I learned that many other Seychellois had followed the same path as him, as the Roman Catholic Church sponsored underprivileged children to undertake higher education in seminaries to become priests.

Gerald Hoarau was a very pleasant person, in his late twenties. He had a gentle, peaceful and relaxed approach to life. I thought he was good-natured and well spoken; he certainly had all the qualities and characteristics that would have qualified him as the perfect priest. He often spoke of football, his favourite pastime, which he played religiously as well as managing a local team. I only loosely followed football compared to the average Italian, but as a proud Sardinian I was a Cagliari Football Club fan.

The meeting went well, as expected. I filled out a questionnaire and was asked a few more questions. Hoarau was satisfied with my answers and confirmed that my work permit would be issued forthwith and that, if I wished, I could start working the following day. Impressed by his remarkable attitude and friendliness, I suggested we meet again for a drink or to watch a local football match. Sometime later, I met him briefly at his office and donated a set of Cagliari Football Club gear for his players that I had procured on a trip to Sardinia, as a gesture to thank him for his kind cooperation.

Chapter fifteen

New Duties

Incredibly pleased to have my papers in order and to be able to start work, I turned up at the office the next morning to start learning the ropes. The first few days on the job left me feeling completely overwhelmed and apprehensive as I sought to correctly accomplish the tasks I had been assigned, in order to satisfy my new boss.

The Ocean Gate House project was in its final stages and coordination of the suppliers and subcontracting works was at full throttle. Mr Floris and I had to spent most of our time at the site. He was a patient teacher, and I was a fast learner. Through my continuous questioning and reading of textbooks, I managed to make up for my lack of experience. I progressively improved my familiarity with the business; interacting with Mr Floris proved to be of great importance to my development. He displayed a serious, business-like attitude towards me; he always kept a straight face. He became a valued mentor, offering his knowledge and skills. After his family went back to Italy, he started to be more relaxed and friendly. Sometimes we socialised a little during the weekends. We would go snorkelling by the reefs as he enjoyed collecting seashells as a hobby. My youthful enthusiasm had inspired him to loosen his provincial self-consciousness, and he appreciated it. Out of the office, he started to call me by my first name, but in the office, he kept it strictly formal and I was addressed by surname only. However, that was fine by me.

One morning, I was on the rooftop of the Ocean Gate House, inspecting the air-conditioning system's water tanks when a worker called me. He said that a woman downstairs was looking for me. Puzzled, I walked down. Parked on the other side of the road was a white Mini with Helena in the driver's seat. It was a pleasant surprise; I had not seen her since dinner at her sister's.

She wanted to know if I was going to Praslin for Christmas. She had heard from Anne that I was. I confirmed that Nick had invited me, and that I was planning to visit him for a few days during the break. But I wondered why she was here, asking me all these questions. I asked if she was going too, but she replied that unfortunately it would be impossible for her to visit, as she had to work throughout the break. I thought how busy and demanding working in tourism at Christmas must be. She asked me to pass on her greetings to Anne and Nick and promptly left. I was left puzzling over her unannounced appearance as I returned to my duties.

Chapter sixteen

Praslin, Christmas 1977

Praslin is the second-largest granitic island in the Seychelles. It has glorious sandy beaches and is the location of the Valle de Mai, believed by locals to be the Garden of Eden. It is also surrounded by numerous beautiful isles and islets.

I would later learn that Signor Cossu was 'at home' on the island because of his numerous investments. Everybody knew of him. He believed that Praslin had the potential to become a future tourist destination and had acquired plots of land along the Cote d'Or, a white sandy, shallow beach that stretched for a few miles. He soon established a profitable real estate business on the island.

His position as Italian consul had acted like a magnet for Italian tourists, who, when visiting the Seychelles would seek to invest in the country as a reason to come back. He would bring them to the island and, once under its charm, and bewitched by the beauty, they were easily persuaded into buying one of his ready-to-go properties. The island thus became popular with Italians, creating a little colony. All of the three major hotels on the seashore were Italian-owned.

The only way to go to Praslin was either by a lengthy schooner voyage of a few hours, or by hopping on a flight, I chose the latter. This was my first visit, and I was completely unaware of what it was going to be like on the island.

I arrived at the domestic terminal and, without many formalities, I exchanged my ticket receipt for a plastic boarding pass.

Unexpectedly, Helena turned up at the check-in desk with a birdcage housing two colourful budgies. They were a present for Nick, would I mind taking it to him? Of course, I accepted the cargo. She was all smiles and chatty, almost flirty I would say.

The tiny eight-seater 'Islander' plane, operated by Inter Island Airways, took off on a wet morning for Praslin. It was rainy season, and at times it would pelt down day and night, non-stop. The small twin propeller aircraft took just 15 minutes to reach our destination, but it wobbled throughout the flight and visibility was poor because of the rain.

The landing was rough. The airstrip was just a patch of grassy land, kept in shape by a bunch of grazing cows. The beaten-earth runway had been covered by red soil and it required constant maintenance, especially during the rainy season. The Islander got to the end of the airstrip and traced back to a small apron area used for parking. The terminal was just a rustic open shed, with a thatched roof made from palm leaves. Again, there were no formalities, everyone just piled out of the plane and, once we were handed our luggage, we were free to continue our onward journeys.

Nick was there to pick me up, and was delighted by the birdcage. After a short drive we reached his rental house at Grand Anse. Anne had arrived a few days earlier.

If I thought the life on Mahé was unhurried and easy going, like driving in the slow lane, I was confronted with an even more extreme version in Praslin. Basic infrastructure was non-existent on the island. There were no tarmac roads, no electricity, water, sewage, no public transport and the island had very few cars. We had travelled back in time! Even the Praslinoise attitude was different from Mahé residents. They had a more leisurely approach: *dolce far niente,* meaning 'how sweet it is to do nothing'.

The petrol station just opposite Nick's rented house sold fuel for the few vehicles on the island, pumped manually via a glass gallon ampoule for cooking burners. At night, individual power generators would come alive to light the most affluent houses.

We went to midnight mass at the nearby church, and the next day I cooked an Italian-inspired Christmas lunch with whatever ingredients we had found at the small grocery shop at the nearby village. Nick and Anne loved it. We had *lasagne al forno*, followed by roast loin of local pork with roasted potatoes and local vegetables. We stayed home because of the rain, enjoying more food and some South African red wine. We entertained ourselves by playing cards, and I got to show off my skills in some classic Italian card games. I skipped sightseeing and returned to Mahé two days later.

Chapter seventeen

Becoming Inseparable

It was a Friday evening and I had just returned from the office. I was ready to unwind for the weekend, but I had not yet decided where to go. After a cool shower, I went to the fridge and pulled out a Sey Brew, the local lager. As I was taking a sip, I heard a car pulling into the garage space, followed by the noisy rattle of the brakes. The garage was on a steep slope, which meant the driver needed to be sure it was secure, lest it roll down the hill. I went out to see who it was and, to my surprise, saw it was Helena's Mini. I welcomed her inside and we immediately began a warm, easy conversation. How was Praslin? And Christmas? She was wearing a floral dress and Yves St Laurent perfume; the scent was captivating. I wondered if she fancied me. I had not made any advances as I had had the impression that she had a boyfriend.

We sat outside on the terrace under an imposing mango tree, both drinking bottles of Sey Brew. She had heard that I was good at cards and asked me to teach her a few new games. The heat and mosquitos forced us inside to the living room and we felt more comfortable once we switched on the air-conditioning. We sat on the rug facing each other while I set out the cards on the small wooden table between us. I am not sure who started it, but it was not long before we found ourselves kissing; after stripping, we moved to the bedroom, making passionate love for the first time. Helena spent the night and left early the next morning to meet arriving clients at the airport.

We started seeing each other more regularly, in between Helena's work schedule, and eventually became inseparable. We were frequently invited to private parties and enjoyed many of the leisure activities that Mahé had to offer. We joined the British expatriate clan for Friday night fish & chips at the Northolme

Hotel, and went for Saturday night dinners and dancing at the romantic, Italian-run Beoliere Night Club. We danced to the sounds of Donna Summer, Michael Jackson, The Bee Gees and Neil Diamond, and I learned the *sega*, a sensual local dance that is like the African version of salsa. It is danced to the beat of a homemade drum and local instruments, along with Creole lyrics, as an expression of Creole culture.

The most crowd-pleasing rendezvous was the Katiolo disco, located just past the airport outside Victoria. One Saturday evening, I went there with couple of new acquaintances and parked the yellow Moke in the unlit, improvised parking area. The place was unpretentious and crowded, and we had fun drinking and dancing. As the evening went on, I slowly began to feel insecure, as people became drunk and loud, and a few brawls broke out. We left early and returned to the car to make our way back home. I started the engine and put the car into first gear, but it did not move. I changed into reverse gear but still the Moke stood inert. Perhaps the gearbox had broken and was not engaging? We laughed! What the heck? I tried and tried, but the car would not move. Finally, we all got out and found a torch, and it was then that we realised that the Moke had been put on cement blocks. Someone had stolen all four wheels. I could not believe it. I swore in languages that no one had even heard of, then I burst into laughter, my friends joining in afterwards as we quickly realised how hilarious the situation was. We got a taxi back home and the car was collected the following day by our mechanics.

Another popular venue with the expatriate community was the Beefeater, a pub located on the edge of the Beau Vallon beach. The publican was a fantastic Welsh guy called Barry, who was fun-loving and full of humour. Conveniently located out of town, it was the rendezvous for all the British professional residents on their afternoons off.

I was not an attentive visitor to pubs, and I only surrendered to the assiduous requests of my friends at the accountancy firm every once in a while. Our South African auditor Terry left the place badly drunk on one occasion. He crossed the road to pee, lost his balance and fell into the roadside ditch. He was missing until he woke up two days later!

On occasional weekends, I would accompany Helena on her some of her duties. She was working for the local travel agency C.U.T. and was a representative of Kuoni, a UK-based tour operator. Her task was to organise the arrivals and departures of holidaymakers to and from the airport, accommodate the needs of the guests and organise activities by selling excursion tours of the islands. She had excellent communication skills and a great ability to involve and engage with guests. She was highly enthusiastic about her job.

I would sometimes join in on excursions and organised tours, or if we were invited by guests for sporadic dinners at the hotels. It was good fun and surprisingly educational because of the diversity of the people we met. Systematically, I learned all of the scheduled airlines flying in and out of the airport, reminding me of my visits to Luton airport in my early twenties.

Chapter eighteen

Local Infrastructure

The roads of Mahé were maintained to a basic but acceptable standard. Traffic was relatively sparse as not many cars were in circulation due to prohibitive import duty costs. However, the introduction of the first TATA buses for the public transportation network was intrusive, as some of the roads were not large enough for two vehicles to pass simultaneously.

The coastal road of Mahé is quite scenic and it was easy to take a tour of the island over a couple of hours. The beautiful mountain route is more challenging and has steep sections where a slow gear is required. Mini Mokes were preferred among tourists and expatriates. However, they also had their disadvantages, like how the seats would get wet during the rainy season and need to be covered by a beach towel.

The communication infrastructure in the Seychelles was relatively basic too. The telephone network was run by Cable & Wireless, and a luxury limited to those who could afford it, including the government, business companies and a select group of private individuals. To call overseas was expensive and we were required to book a call at the Cable & Wireless office in Victoria. The local state-controlled radio station would air three times a day – morning, midday, and evening. They would broadcast the news in English, French and Creole. No TV networks existed. Radio was the fastest method of spreading information and news; it was also used for obituaries, the only way to inform relatives of their recently deceased family members or friends. A popular pastime was gathering information and then passing on grossly inflated rumours by word of mouth, known as *radio bambou*. Gossip was locally known as *kankan*. Water and the electricity supply were adequate and generally reliable. The main hospital at Victoria was run efficiently by British doctors and well-trained local nurses and free to attend for all countrymen.

To this day, Victoria remains the focal point of the country; all the functions of the government are based in the town. It becomes lively from morning until about five in the afternoon, usually quieting down for the evening. However, it would become busier with the arrival of foreign navy ships at the port. It was always an event when the crew came ashore in search of pleasure and a little adventure. The local ladies would turn up in full force for extra cash and the odd night out, and Victoria's bars and restaurants remained open until late to entertain the impromptu but very welcome guests.

Chapter nineteen

A Pot Pourri of Flavours

Life in Seychelles meant I had to readapt my eating habits, as the country did not provide much of the Italian cuisine I had grown up with. However, it was a journey of discovery, in a place where Europe meets Africa and Asia. The Seychelles offered a pot pourri of diverse flavours.

The staple Creole food was fish and boiled rice, flavoured with chillies and curry power. There was no fresh milk or real coffee, so the local vanilla-flavoured tea was a delicious substitute, sweetened with thick, glue-like condensed milk. The types of tropical fruit were endless – I had never seen or tasted any of them before, except for bananas.

Coming from Sardinia, curries and chillies were words I had never heard of. My mum's cuisine was very much Mediterranean-flavoured and delicately seasoned with aromatic herbs. Predictably, my favourite restaurants in Victoria turned out to be the Continental, run by two Neapolitan guys, and La Tartaruga Felice at Mont Fleuri.

My first experience of curry was at a banquet at the residence of the Indian high commissioner. Because of a connection of Helena's brother, we were invited to a dinner party during Diwali celebrations. The high commissioner's estate was above Victoria, in the prestigious Sans Souci neighbourhood. We had never been to any Indian gatherings previously, but we had been told of the importance of the occasion. It was the highlight of the social calendar, and I looked forward to the chance to mingle with this sort of crowd.

Upon arrival at the residence, staff were on hand to direct the guests to the parking area. The grounds were immaculately manicured and adorned with hundreds of lights and decorations. A large terrace overlooking the town was illuminated with lanterns along its edge. It was a wonderful sight to see.

The crème de la crème of all Mahé was in attendance, including a fair number of the top VIPs among the Indian community. Guests were perfectly dressed for the occasion. There was quite a cultural mixture of attire, as they were all wearing their finest clothes. The ladies wore silky, shining saris or were wrapped in colourful sarongs, with glitzy, heavy gold earrings and bracelets. The men wore tight-fitting long Jodhpur coats or Nehru jackets, usually in cream or white, with turbans or western shirts.

Impeccably-attired waiters wearing regal uniforms complete with turbans served guests drinks and appetizers. By the terrace, a long table was set, decorated with fine tablecloths and adorned meticulously with dishes of different sizes and a display of food so ornate that one would not want to disrupt it.

Once dinner was announced, the guests queued to be served. It was a standing buffet banquet, and the sight of the food was making my mouth water. I followed Helena and filled my plate with as much as I could squeeze onto it. We found a spot in one corner to feast on the delicious food.

I was starving, having not eaten all day. Ungraciously, I scooped up a spoonful of food from my plate and stuffed it into my mouth. As soon as the food touched by lips, my mouth caught fire and my tongue went numb. The heat travelled down through my throat and deep inside my stomach. It all happened in a matter of seconds. I had never felt such a sensation before. I coughed the remaining of the food out and gasped for Helena's help. The burning was so intense that I panicked and screamed loudly. The commotion got the attention of nearby guests and they all turned to watch me gasping desperately for air.

A waiter showed up within minutes, handed me a cold glass of milk and told me to sip it. I slowly swallowed the chilled milk. As it went down my throat, I felt the milk gradually relieve the burning sensation.

My initiation to these hot and spicy flavours was not a pleasant one, considering that my spice tolerance level was apparently zero! Such an awkward experience in such opulent surroundings left me feeling horribly embarrassed. Even Helena admitted that the dishes were very spicy, saying that the Seychellois, in general, did not eat curries that hot.

The evening was still enjoyable as it was an entirely new experience, and culturally educational in so many ways. It all culminated in a firework display, with a thousand lights glittering across the clear night sky.

* * *

One evening, on my way to the house at Glacis, I stopped to get some provisions at a grocery shop by the side of the road. Displayed by the door were some unusually long, dark yellow bananas that I had never seen before. Bananas were the only tropical fruit I knew of, but my mum never bought them, as they were awfully expensive in Sardinia. As a teenager working at hotels, I had eaten them and found them delicious. Holding my tins of baked beans and a loaf of bread, I asked the shopkeeper for two large bananas and planned to eat them for dessert.

After a lousy "beans on toast" dinner, I ventured on to my culinary discovery: this overwhelmingly big banana. The peeling was not as easy as I thought it should be, and the skin was hard and tough to remove. After finally removing it, I started to nibble the banana. I noticed it had a woody texture, an unusual stodginess, and a complete lack of sweetness. But, hey, what did I know about tropical fruit? So, I ate one whole.

A few hours later, I had a noxious bellyache and indigestion all night. To relieve the pain, I took some tablets but barely slept. The following morning, I told the story at the office, expecting sympathy, but everyone laughed at me. They were cooking bananas! Yes, 'Banana St Jacques', that can't be eaten unless cooked.

I later tasted Banana St Jacques boiled with breadfruit, cassava or sweet potatoes in coconut milk, sugar, nutmeg, and vanilla to make a creamy sauce called *ladob*, traditionally served for dessert. It was delicious!

Helena slowly introduced me to more mild curries, such as chicken curry with coconut milk and a variety of the Creole cuisine that she had adapted for a more delicate palate. She made wonderful fish dishes were spiced with hot chillies but my favourite – grilled red snapper, *bourgeois* – was also spiced the Mediterranean way and very delicious too.

People did try to tempt me to try fruit bat curry, *kari sousouri*, and turtle meat, which are rare delicacies, and the more common salty fish in moringa leaf soup, *bouyon bred,* but I categorically refused.

Chapter twenty

Socialist Vision

President René was busy implementing his socialist vision: raising minimum wages, improving housing and health facilities, and increasing the number of state schools.

It seemed as though the lives of the Seychellois improved quickly and they were in favour of his political aims. On the surface, it appeared as though René's policies did not favour any particular foreign power, and he promoted a friendly relationship with all nations. He created a centralised government with power concentrated on him and was nicknamed 'the boss'.

As his new government settled in, the British civil servants who were still working in various departments were gradually replaced with René's associates. Experience and qualifications were not a requisite.

President René's regime continued relentlessly on the path of socialism. Private schools were abolished, and the National Youth Service (NYS) was created. Children aged 11 to 16 were sent to military-style camps for education or indoctrination, Cuban style. The creation of the NYS had parents and students in revolt, as demonstrations gathered in the streets of Victoria. Parents who had previously endorsed René were now strongly opposed to the idea that their children would effectively be interned for two years on the outer island of Coetivy.

Under the pretence of revolution and nationalism, René announced the adoption of Creole as the third official language of the Seychelles, without any kind of public debate to discuss the benefits, merits or costs. He viewed French and English as the languages of the upper-class and wanted to be seen by the people as their popular leader, the 'liberator' who spoke the same 'mother-tongue'. It was a defining moment of strength, showing that he was the people's president, 'son kamarade'. This led to the creation of the Creole Institute, which sought to codify what is essentially an oral, phonetic language into a written one. It instantly created a population of illiterates as no one could write or read it. Financial resources were committed to the programme at public schools, at the expense of learning English and French. Introducing Creole at primary schools was also very confusing as children had to revise their usage, which was mainly oral.

I learned Creole fast. The elementary French I learned at school, followed by three months practice at my first summer job at the hotel helped – the Ala Birdi Hotel had always been full of French tourists. I learned how to swear first, and the rest followed after. I realised that, in order to earn the respect of the Seychellois, I needed to be able to answer them in their mother tongue. I know that my accent and vocabulary was nowhere near perfect, but it helped; the workers knew that I understood them. It was crucial when working at the sites. Off duty, at shops and hotels, I had fun showing off my knowledge of the language, especially with women, who benevolently found my accent amusing.

Work began at seven a.m., from Monday to Friday. When in the country, Mr Floris would take his lunch breaks with me at the Pirates Arms, infrequently joined by Mr Perrillo. Centrally located in Victoria, it was the popular rendezvous and an iconic place for tourists, expatriates and local influential people alike. The Cossu Group owned the hotel complex. The restaurant was a goldmine, open all day and always remarkably busy! Occupying part of the hotel, the large, open veranda was built entirely in local takamaka wood. Slightly elevated from the road, it had a rustic, colonial feel, with wooden-louvered windows across the front side. It was not just a place for a coffee, a light snack or spot for lunch: this was the town piazza. You could chat and gather news, divulge rumours and catch up on the day's gossip there. From its open veranda overlooking Victoria's Independence Avenue, one could watch island life pass by, witness a business deal, form new friendships and socially interact with locals or help tourists with their inquiries.

The hotel foyer had a souvenir shop, a barbershop and an Aeroflot office (the Russian airline). A German man named Fritz was the hotel's manager. Signor Cossu's private consular office was strategically located there, as was his travel business, Blue Safari.

If there were no immediate setbacks or deadline commitments, I would usually finish work at around five p.m. After driving home for a change of clothes, I would go to Beau Vallon beach for a swim and a stroll by the shoreline. This became such a routine that I would meet the same people, an unusual crowd of expatriate civil servants and local merchants, usually Indian, along with embassy staff. Away from the watchful eyes of the Pirates Arms circle, everyone seemed to be chattier and more at ease to indulge in conversation and *kankan*. I found it all very intriguing and thrilling.

Chapter twenty one

Laissez Faire

As soon as the Ocean Gate House project broke ground, trade unions began threatening SOGIS with strikes and revolt, harassing us daily at our sites. It disrupted the performance and reliability of our workforce. This was the only major project going in town, and we were targeted as a result; the growing bureaucracy of these newly empowered cronies was increasingly frustrating daily business.

I observed the performance of our workers and concluded that they were underachieving and actively underperforming on the standards we were used to as Italians. But I soon realised that each country had different conditions and approaches that determined how a worker performed. For example, the Sardinian workforce, because of the weather during the long summer months, is less productive than workers in the cooler northern part of Italy are. However, the underachievement of the Seychelles' workforce was partly due to the Creole philosophy of *'travayer pa oule travay'*, 'workers do not want to work.' In general, this *laissez faire* attitude was the main culprit – as well as the intense tropical heat. There was no hurry to do anything, no need to live by European expectations, because they were content with their lifestyle and the Seychellois pace of life. There was no desire to follow western ways of doing things, at least not yet.

We had to confront the trade unions head-on and after weeks of frustrated negotiations, an arrangement was drawn up between the Ministry of Labour, the Unions and SOGIS to raise minimum wages and salaries as a constructive collaboration, and a way to see more progress.

However, armed with the fact that President René was their comrade, the union leaders were still in search of back-handers in exchange for peace and quiet at the site, and they became more aggressive with their demands as we resisted their pressure. Mr Floris was adamant that we be open-minded with our workforce and conduct business in a fair manner. He felt it was never right to corrupt someone with money. Stay away from politicians, he used to warn me, reminding me of Babbu. I agreed entirely.

Months later, the trade unions merged with the Ministry of Labour and their abusive tactics were clipped. SOGIS was able to breathe again for a while. We had to adapt fast to the volatile situation.

New ministers were appointed within the new government. However, the principal secretaries, who were mostly Seychellois, were the most qualified non-political civil servants still practising ethical standards. They had served during the British administration, with the Mancham Government and now under René.

The principal secretary of the Ministry of Labour, Mr David Wong, helped us negotiate an agreement with the unions, personally attending the signing of the agreement. A Seychellois of Chinese origin, he was well-educated and had spent some time studying in England. Originally a teacher, by then he had been working for the government for many years and was well respected and trusted by the establishment. He loved Chinese cooking and an invitation to his dinner parties was highly sought-after. We later became good friends. He was a lustful reader of *Playboy* magazine; at his request, I discreetly brought copies for him every time I returned to the country. The circulation of any form of pornography was illegal in Seychelles but I managed to smuggle them in my suitcase, risking trouble at the airport. He happily shared them among his circle of best friends, because of their rarity on the island.

Chapter twenty two

The Uniqueness of an Island

Among his array of assets, Signor Cossu had a wonderful two-masted schooner for his amusement and entertainment. The vessel had been built locally at the La Digue boatyard, the master boat builders in the country. Apparently, it was modelled on old drawings of similar boats that had sailed these waters, producing a one-of-kind schooner with a distinct style. It was beautifully handcrafted, piece by piece; no machinery of any kind was used for its construction. This was his pride and joy, his *Britannia*, and when on board Signor and Signora Cossu dressed the part, keeping up their glamorous lifestyle, with impeccable attire that strictly followed rules of dressing in a 'maritime' fashion: light clothing to match with the crew in their white and blue navy uniforms. Signor Cossu was 'Master and Commander.' Signora Cossu was in charge of the hospitality, ensuring the utmost comfort for their guests; she meticulously checked every detail, from cabin cleaning to the catering service. She could at times be an ostentatious and difficult lady, and always enforced her demands in a charming yet determined way.

I was once invited to cruise the Praslin archipelago, an invitation that I had to regrettably decline due to my seasickness. Signor Cossu had named his schooner after the island of Curieuse, which lies just off Praslin. He claimed it was unique due to the flora and fauna, which was found nowhere else. He never missed the opportunity to visit the island when cruising with guests and this became the cruise's highlight. It was a must-see island. I was not entirely sure if I should believe him as I had realised, he would sometimes exaggerate his statements a little. However, his talk got me curious, and I decided to mark Curieuse on my list of places to visit at the first opportunity.

I needed to find an outboard boat that would take me across the stretch of water between Praslin and Curieuse. As I set about organising the visit to the island, finding a boat became my mission.

The local fishermen at Cote d'Or only had pirogues, usually paddled by three men, and they would not adventure over the reef barrier, only setting down their fish traps in the seabed, in shallow waters within the reef. After all, Seychellois were generally not good swimmers.

I became acquainted with a Mr Delpeche, a Praslinoise, who had recently returned to Praslin after retiring, after long service as a civil servant with the government in Mahé. He had a freestanding house on an outcrop promontory just before Anse Possession that overlooked the sea and the island of Curieuse. He came several times to our building site asking for materials to do some repairs at his house. I mentioned my quest to get to the island, and he did not hesitate a moment before offering to drop me there and back whenever I was ready.

The following weekend, Helena, a couple of friends and I flew to Praslin to carry out this expedition to the island that none of us had ever set foot on, so eloquently described by Signor Cossu as 'paradisiacal'. Early the next morning, we drove to the house of Mr Depeche, who was up and waiting for us. We boarded his small boat, equipped with an outboard motor, and off we went. The weather was perfect, and the sea was calm and placid, so we sailed in straight line at a reasonable speed and in less than ten minutes had reached our destination.

Mr Delpeche dropped us on the beautiful white sandy beach of Anse St. José; thanks to the excellent sea conditions and lack of waves, we disembarked easily. He had been before and had drawn us a map on a piece of paper, as though it was a treasure hunt. He said he would return around five in the afternoon to pick us up from the other side of the island.

Anse St. José is a short stretch of pure coralline sand and crystal-clear water. It was low tide when we arrived and very seductive; we felt wonderful and ready to experience what we all anticipated would be an amazing expedition. The morning sunshine was a good omen for the day ahead, and we settled in and relaxed on top of the beach's sandy bank that edged two sides of the shoreline. As the island was uninhabited, the girls decided to strip down to their bikini and enjoy a sunbathing session. I scouted the area around us. The beach was fringed by huge takamaka, tall casuarina trees and overgrown vegetation, too bushy to see through. I returned to the 'girls club'. They were in full chitchat mode so I decided to have a dip and go snorkelling. I plunged into the pristine, clear waters to discover that part of the seabed was just white coral sand and patchy seagrass in green and rusty shades that slowly waved with the current. The seabed looked perforated with holes, hiding spots and dwellings for small creatures but it seemed unusually deserted, with only a few silverfishes in the shallows. I swam a little further and suddenly saw the sandy bottom tremble before two large, previously camouflaged stingrays emerged., They majestically flapped and swivelled around me, completely unthreatened, before moving off into the blue of the ocean in a flash. In a matter of seconds, they were gone and I was alone again, so I swam back ashore.

The girls had not moved from the spot I left them in, and were chatting about office gossip. The sun was high and hot, and it was time for us to get moving. The girls dressed and we cut through the undergrowth reaching a flat plot of land, the site of an old leprosy hospital. Back in 1939, after an outbreak of leprosy, patients had been brought here to isolate them from the rest of the population.

The complex stood in silence, abandoned and in ruins. It was engulfed by wild vegetation, as nature had taken over, but a two-storey wooden dwelling remained visible – the doctors' house. We decided to take a look inside. As the wooden floor was cracked and rotting, we had to be careful where to take our next step. Tree branches and roots had entered the building and, from the high branches, trumpet vines cascaded inside leaving a blanket of large, glossy, dark green leaves, with delightful flowers of a light lavender colour and a dark venation. A fast-growing creeper that climbs by way of rootlets clinging to just about anything, trumpet vine is an invasive weed that chokes out any other plants. It was unsafe to enter, and the girls refused to go any further, returning to a courtyard in between the buildings. I felt brave enough to continue exploring and carefully entered a large room. I froze at the sight of red spiders, which were common on the islands; but here they were enormous and had created webs interlinking with others that spanned across the room. I chickened out and retreated, my bravery having proved to be short-lived. The dampness of the undergrowth was perfect territory for crawling creatures, and we soon realised that the place was swarming with millipedes and the more venomous centipedes. The flipflops we were wearing did not offer much protection, so we kept our eyes well open and remained on guard. I had been stung by a centipede in Mahé and it was painful as hell, paralysing my arm for several minutes.

We looked around for a little longer, found the single track marked on our map and proceeded inland. Initially, we made our way through the undergrowth but once the path went uphill and more distinctly marked, the shrubbery changed. Latanier dwarf palms were seconded by the more prominent tall cocoplum trees, with long upright branches bearing white-purple fruit. We picked a few ripe ones, as Helena said they were edible. I had a bite and found it a bit sharp-tasting; it had a big seed in the middle, a sort of sweet-fluffy cotton candy.

On our way, still climbing, the tropical heat got thicker, signalling that the rain was not far off. And just like that, it poured down, suddenly heavy; this was unexpected it is not uncommon in the tropics. We were unprepared and, with no cover, we resorted to cutting the latanier palm leaves and using them as umbrellas! We laughed at each other, sopping wet, and wished we had a camera to seize the moment.

As we got to the brow of the hill, the rain stopped as suddenly as it had come. We finally reached the southern part of Laraie Bay, a vast swamp area full of mangroves, formerly inhabited by crocodiles, which were now extinct from the islands. The dry ground around the mangroves were home to large, red land crabs that fed from the mangroves, scavenging for fruit and especially for turtle eggs. The bigger the hole, the bigger the lodger; we teased them with a stick, hanging some bread from it, keen to see their real size. The mangroves were also a nursery for a number of sea creatures who had found residence in the shallow waters between the roots, enabling them to hide from predators.

Mr Delpeche had told us about the two ways to reach our destination at Anse Papaie: via a granite wall across the bay or a track around the mangrove swamp.

The wall had been built to create a pond reserve, a sanctuary for the hawksbill turtles, a critically endangered species sought after for their meat, eggs and shells. However, the marine project had run out of funds, and the conservation project had been abandoned.

We decided to take the short cut through the stone wall as it seemed more practical. With the mid-morning heat beating down on us and in our flipflops, we started to cross over to the other side. The wall had visible wear and tear but gave us no reason to be concerned; there was water on either side and the mangrove swamp had petered out. We reached almost halfway when we discovered a large hole where the wall had collapsed. It was too high for us to drop into the water and swim over and there were strong currents flowing from the lagoon into the open sea. We were stuck. There were some wooden planks on either side, as if someone had used them to get across, but the gap seemed wider than they were long, so the planks were impracticable for the crossing. As we pondered our options, we sat on the wall and watched beautifully colourful fish feeding as the tide rushed back out to sea. It was an amazing display: the fish rushed for the best spot and then skilfully manoeuvred to remain idle, almost immobile, with their open mouths swallowing as much food they could handle, before giving up the spot to their mates. After the spectacle, we decided to find another way across.

We tracked back to the mangroves and, with no path to follow, had to circle the turtle pond through to the swamps. We were confronted with a demanding landscape – the soil was cracked, like a chessboard, but it looked dry and accessible. Once we started walking across this terrain, we found ourselves sinking into wet ground. As our feet sank deeper into the mud, we had to move away from the mangroves. Sticking out from the soil were stilt roots, which were like breathing pipes for the mangroves. Some were tall and visible, others emerged no more than a few centimetres above ground. Wearing flipflops made our walk extremely arduous, although they protected our feet from the sharp stilts; pulling them out from the sticky mud was rather laborious. How painful it must have been for the fugitive Papillon running barefoot through the swamps of French Guyana!

We reached more solid ground, heaving sighs of relief. We had not expected such a troublesome and hideous passage.

I was the frontman, making the good and bad decisions, while the trio behind me complained when things did not turn out according to the plan. They would have preferred to sunbathe by the beach rather than struggle in a muddy swamp.

We spotted a giant tortoise; as we walked towards it, we encountered a whole colony, peaceful and freely grazing about. They are enormous, like creatures from *Jurassic Park*, and can live for hundred years. These creatures belong to a different world. The colony here were natives of Aldabra and are now a protected species.

At first, they looked intimidating, because of their size, but they are actually docile, friendly creatures. They are, however, especially agile with their telescopic necks, extending them to unbelievable heights when grazing for the fresh new sprouts of the mangrove trees. They like to be stroked on their necks and I unrepentantly rode one by stroking with a stick on its dorsal shell!

Finally, we reached firmer ground leading into a valley of tall palm trees, the endemic and unique Coco de Mer; this was the only other location besides Valle de Mai in Praslin where palms flourished. However, the palm trees here stood in the open air, whereas at Valle de Mai they were covered by a canopy of tropical foliage. We climbed high above to see spectacular views over the valley, the sea and Praslin in the distance. We sat in the shadow of the giant palms while eating our lunch and eventually made it to Anse Papaie, walking along the beach north towards an impressive granite rock formation. The pink granite boulders stand upright, like spikes, from the white coralline sand, and have been sculpted by the forces of nature into art forms, creating pieces of magic. The site reminded me of the granite rock formation of the Gallura region, in the northeast of Sardinia.

The girls were in a better mood by now. Exhausted, we lay on the sandy beach absorbing the afternoon sun, but I could not resist a last dive. I had been told shoals of green humphead parrotfish were commonly found in this part of the reef. After a short swim into the lagoon, I reached the fringing reef at the drop-off. The visibility was perfect; there were small, colourful species of fish feeding on meadows of seagrass, but the corals were not as lively and vivid as at other sites; it was actually quite uninteresting at first. However, it was not long before I spotted a number of humphead parrotfish appearing from the blue and coming my way. They are indiscriminate fish, travelling in shoals, capable of savagely devouring the coral reef by crashing into the coral with their heads and feeding with the help of their powerful jaw. They are also responsible for creating an awful lot of white sand once they expel the ingested coral.

It was my lucky day, as a solitary Napoleon fish also appeared. I recognised him from the hump on the front of his head, similar to the Napoleon-style hat, hence the name. He remained at a distance, apparently admiring the distraction of his associates, as they do not share the same habits nor diet. He displayed curiosity as he approached me. A green-blue colour, he was rather large with large plump lips, like a Botox treatment gone very wrong! Eventually, the humphead parrotfish disappeared into the depths of the ocean and so did my Napoleon fish friend. It was time to return ashore.

Mr Delpeche turned up with his boat as arranged and we reluctantly left the unspoilt island wilderness. I agreed with Signor Cossu about his love of the island; it was awesome and mesmerising. About a year later, in 1979, the Seychelles Government declared the island and its surrounding sea a Marine National Park.

Chapter twenty three

Helena's Brother

I met Helena's brother, Guy, informally on a few occasions at their mum's during his rushed lunch breaks. Secretly I was hoping for an invitation to his house so I could get to know him properly. Helena respected him greatly, partly because he was her elder brother, but also for his academic achievements.

Their relationship reminded me of my own with my elder brother, Bruno. There was a 14-year age gap between us, and I had not lived with him growing up, as he had left for his military service when I was about five years old, moving afterwards to Turin for work. I had no recollection of him at all until he moved back to Terralba when I was in my twenties. I found reconnecting with a sibling after being apart for such a long time hard work and time-consuming. I had missed out on all the bonding experiences of living under the same roof with Bruno. For me, the closeness was not there initially but eventually, things got better, our shared blood quickly binding us together.

Guy had left Seychelles at the age of 24 to work as an apprentice accountant for a rubber plantation in Borneo. He then went to Australia to study economics at Melbourne University. After being away for some 18 years, he returned to the Seychelles in 1974 and entered employment with the government.

We were invited for lunch at his newly built, modern-looking villa 'Charlotte', which was located on the hillside at Ma Costance, halfway between Victoria and the north-eastern point of Mahé. The access road proved quite a challenge for my little Mini Moke, with the steep, half-paved ascent that was common in hillside residences across most of the island. He had just moved in a few months earlier with his new English girlfriend, Sue, who was working at the town's PR office for the Ministry of Tourism on a two-year contract.

Sue made a great effort and served, with the help of the maid, a beautiful Creole lunch set on the new takamaka-wood dining table, all accompanied by Mozart's Symphony No.40. It turned out that Guy had quite a collection of classical records, featuring all his favourite composers, which he played on a state-of-the-art record player that no one was allowed to touch. His classical music knowledge impressed me; he was familiar with so many composers and the trivia relating to them – he even had his own one-hour broadcast slot dedicated to classical music on Radio Seychelles!

After lunch, we sat on the veranda overlooking the inner islands and continued the conversation over a few glasses of wine. Soon enough, Guy began testing my knowledge of composers and Greek mythology, which were apparently his best subjects. I was prepared. I had been studying, as Helena had warned me to. It turned out that we got on very well and I passed his test!

As we made to leave, he said that we should get together more often, and so we did. On future occasions, he would relay tales of his trips around the world and his love of ballet that had led him to see shows at Covent Garden, La Scala, the Bolshoi, the Metropolitan, the Verona Arena and many others.

Guy was becoming an influential figure in his role as secretary of state for finance. Being non-political and non-aligned to René's policies gave him close links and direct access to 'the boss', as René held both the title of president and minister of finance. He was appointed first chairman and governor of the newly established Central Bank. When travelling, if asked for his identity, he used Seychelles bank notes as his business card, as his signature was on them!

As his government duties were increasing with more chairmanships and bigger responsibilities, he was happy to relax and be with us on Saturdays for dinner or Sunday for lunch, sipping some wine from the clear, imperfect, handmade Murano glasses that he had bought in Venice. He loved describing the experience of haggling in Italian at the glassware shop for them, laughing at the loud shopkeeper and his wild, heavily gesticulated performance; 'so passionately *Italian*', he remarked.

Chapter twenty four

Nello Africanus

One of the people who turned up regularly at Beau Vallon beach after work for a swim and a friendly chat was an old Italian, a funny chap, by the name of Nello. We became good friends.

He had left Italy in his early twenties to work as a carpenter for a large Italian construction company building aqueduct infrastructure systems in Tanzania. He had rarely returned to Italy, except to visit family. To escape a harsh life under the Nyerere socialist regime in Tanzania, he had found refuge in the Seychelles at the age of sixty-something.

He was of average build and quite slim, with remarkably thick brown hair for his age. He dressed smartly, in short-sleeved shirts and long summer trousers. We used to make fun of the way he wore his trousers belted high above the waist with his shirt always tucked in. He had such skinny legs, we compared him to a white stork. His constant watchfulness was also extraordinary. After spending such a long time in the bush of Tanzania, his head twitched frequently as if alerted by the proximity of danger or prey.

He lived in a beautiful Creole-style house at Le Niol, in the hills above Beau Vallon. The house belonged to a Californian who rented it out to him to ensure its upkeep. Nello's personality fit well with the property, as both had a sense of enigma and secrecy.

The Creole architecture of the house expressed mystery with its sharply sloping roof and skylights that stood out like nuns' coifs. Access to the house was from the main road, via a track that sloped into a paved parking area, with hedges of flowering shrubs and exotic trees. The courtyard featured large Nido powdered milk tins that had been painted in bright colours and recycled as flowerpots, strung along the pathway leading to the veranda. The back garden was lush with fruit trees and hibiscus in a variety of colours. Orchids were wrapped in coconuts husks or embedded into the takamaka tree trunks for shade and humidity. The Seychellois gardener took pride in keeping the surrounding areas clean and attractive.

The house revealed its originality through its interior decoration; built in local wood throughout, it was full of the owner's memorabilia from past travels and pictures of happy family memories. The living room was the central focus of the house, with French glass doors that led to a large, open veranda with a balustrade and the 100-year-old trunk of a takamaka tree growing through it. It was a sight to remember, and the views were spectacular through the shaded tropical gardens to the blue sea in the distance.

Nello had opened a shop close to the clock tower in town called African Jewels and Curios. It was a remarkably successful little business, as tourists who visited Victoria flocked there to buy quality souvenirs. He mainly dealt in ivory, coral, turtle shells and ebony objects, which he turned into much sought-after pieces of jewellery. If he wasn't too busy, he would visit the office for a mid-morning cup of tea and *kankan* or perhaps the beach if it was after five.

Helena and I were frequently invited to his charming house for improvised Italian meals. We listened to his many stories about his days in Africa as we lay on the comfortable sofas in the veranda admiring the amazing views. His life in Tanzania had been very adventurous; he had lived in the north of the country between Arusha and Moshi in the foothills of Mount Kilimanjaro.

In the early 1960s, while working with an Italian construction company as a carpenter, Nello was asked to help with building part of the set of the movie *Hatari*, which was filmed on a plain north of Arusha. He was featured as an extra in some of the scenes and even met John Wayne and the Italian actress, Elsa Martinelli. Apparently, she was terrified of all the wildlife, including the flies! Nello burst out laughing when describing the scenes of the baby elephants chasing Elsa Martinelli at the Indian emporium, destroying a part of the shot. He was stationed outside with fellow onlookers, laughing their heads off watching the elephants disobey the director's wishes, leading to several reshoots of the scene.

Nello eventually reached the end of his contract with the Italian firm and decided to diversify his work. He successfully managed to gain a rare mining license. The hills around Mount Kilimanjaro are known for their semi-precious stone tanzanite. He teamed up with an American partner and employed a few locals to mine the land. Months later, he discovered that he would never make a fortune out of the mining business because the miners had been stealing part of the retrieved stones, making it unprofitable to keep running the venture. It was more efficient and cost-effective to buy the rough stones that had been stolen from other miners. As word spread, he found queues every evening at his home; he purchased the stolen rough stones for cash and passed them off as being from his own mine, using his license.

When Nello and his partner had amounted enough stones to fill a suitcase, they decided to make a trip to the USA and sell the gemstones to the highest bidder. His American partner took charge of the task. After saying their goodbyes at Kilimanjaro Airport, he boarded the aircraft and Nello didn't hear from him again until years later, when he received an invitation with an air ticket attached to visit his partner in the USA. Nello decided to go and confront him. When asked about his share, the American said that he had nothing to give as he had spent it all, accompanying this with a shrug of the shoulders. Nello told us all of this with a smile across his face. Somehow, he was not bitter or angry about the whole thing, constantly giggling while telling the story.

Chapter twenty five

The Bird Sanctuary Island, Easter 1978

Helena had a complimentary weekend voucher for Bird Island Lodge, located on the northernmost of the archipelago. Flat and made from coral, Bird Island is home to a coconut plantation and millions of sooty terns that nest there. We decided to spend Easter weekend there.

We took off on a clear, beautiful morning. The Inter Island Airways flight on the Trislander was busier than usual; the pilot directed the propellered aircraft north, across the ocean, for the 30-minute flight. As we flew over the inner islands that surrounded Victoria, the scenery was as impressively beautiful as the first time I had seen it. Lagoons and white sandy beaches fringed by coconut palm trees encircled the island. We landed on a tiny airstrip at Bird Island and checked into one of the bungalows at the Lodge.

The next morning, we dreamily walked down to a remote part of the island holding hands, a pleasant stroll through the coconut tree plantation to the other side of the Lodge. The beach was deserted, and we lazily settled down at our chosen spot. We were surrounded by untouched nature; there was not one soul around.

The shallow lagoon in front of us was undeniably seductive. Spontaneously, we took off our clothes, throwing ourselves into the placid warm waters. Chasing each other playfully, we breathlessly returned to the white beach and lay on its soft velvet sand, enjoying its smooth caress our on naked bodies. We made love, unaware of the thousands of sooty terns floating in the air above us. We stayed in this heaven-on-earth for hours, relaxing and admiring the birds' fishing skills.

The island had been a bird sanctuary for hundreds of years. Flocks of sooty tern first arrive in March, creating a million-strong colony in just a few weeks. They lay their eggs everywhere – in old and new nests, on treetops, at the foot of trees, on branches, on the grass or on pebbles – you name it, they are not shy. Thousands of bird's eggs are also collected for human consumption in May, for egg curry, a Creole delicacy.

After a romantic candlelit dinner at the Lodge's open-air restaurant, we cautiously picked our way through the vegetation, along the path, back to our bungalow, covering our heads to make sure we were not shat on by the roosting birds settling down for the evening! We sat on our veranda and stared out to the ocean, admiring the stars glittering in the indigo sky. The warm breeze was pleasurable, the air filled with the sweet scent of frangipani, jasmine, and hibiscus. It was inebriating and we intensely made love again.

Chapter twenty six

The Sardinian Rowbinson Crusoe

Signor Cossu had told me about a Terralbese man who was living in Praslin. It was unbelievable; it was a small world indeed. His name was Vargiolu. I had never heard of such a name, and I was quite certain it was not native to my hometown. However, my curiosity took hold of me, and I decided that I would find him at the first free opportunity while I was in Praslin. He lived in Anse Lazio; an area completely isolated as no roads led there.

I arrived in Praslin early one morning and was at the building site by seven o'clock; Nick and the foreman were expecting me and, while we had a list of construction issues to deal with, we had completed all our tasks by eleven. I had nothing planned for the rest of the day and it occurred to me that I had enough time for a visit to Anse Lazio.

I asked Louis, the foreman, about the ride and told him of my intentions. He considered my office attire and politely suggested that maybe I was not equipped for such a trek. Jeans, soft shoes and no hat were certainly enough for a walk in the park, but not for a trip into dense tropical vegetation! The walk was only about one and a half miles though; so, I thought that surely it would not be a problem.

The track terminated at the beach of Anse Boudin, with stunning views over the island of Curieuse. Scattered about were several shacks, rustic wood cabins with *latanier*-thatched roofs, as well as a small grocery shop, several solid wooden structures and a Roman Catholic church built in concrete with a high roof. It made for an unexpected village.

I parked the Moke under the shade of a *bois noir* tree and walked on foot into the jungle, following a rough path. The start of the trail was sheltered by a variety of imposing trees; I noticed other shacks dispersed throughout the jungle. As I advanced deeper, the route became narrower, steeper and hillier. The tall, shady trees disappeared leaving patchy open spaces that were definitely off the beaten track.

The journey was challenging, as my shoes did not have much grip on the fine red soil and the midday sun was at its zenith. I was perspiring heavily and had forgotten to bring any water with me. I had no hat and there were no trees around to provide shade from the heat.

The hilltop vegetation was full of low-rise, rust-coloured *latanier* palm trees and bushes, as the area had been devastated by a fire a few years back. Once at the top, it was possible to admire the cove of Anse Lazio below, with spectacular views of the bay and its incredible, translucent, turquoise water.

Because of the conditions I found myself in, my observations from the hilltop were cut short as I rushed downhill and searched for shade to escape the relentless midday sun. The downhill walk was easy enough and finally I reached the flat soil of a coconut plantation. I stopped and saw a small pile of harvested coconuts, noticing a long, pointed stick embedded deeply in the ground right next to it—the tool used by locals to remove the husk of the coconut. I had been shown and learned what seemed a strenuous task and managed to de-husk two coconuts. Once de-husked, I slowly beat them onto a stone until they cracked into two parts. Raising the halves to my lips with my head tilted back, I managed to suck out the water, alleviating my thirst. Sitting under the shade of a coconut tree, I paused and recharged my energy.

Lined by coconut trees, the bay was deserted, and its beach of soft, white sand looked unsullied. At each end, the bay met a tumble of granite boulders and, after walking along the beach, I noticed a lonely house built inland, alongside a freshwater lake.

I thought this must be where my fellow Terralbese man lived. I found a narrow trail leading to the house and made my way across a rickety wooden bridge to cross a waterway that ran through the property. As I walked towards the house, a couple of dogs surrounded me and started barking. I was not worried about the noise they made. I tried to quiet them down but to no avail; teasing them did not help, either. Suddenly, a man appeared just outside the rustic, granite house. Still at a distance, I shouted that I was looking for Mr Vargiolu, and he shouted back: 'That is me!' The dogs were silenced by his firm instructions, and I neared the house to introduce myself. He had not seen a stranger's face for months, he said, and had not been expecting to, but he was nonetheless very pleased to see me.

Vargiolu lived in the house with his wife and handicapped adult son. 'Robinson Crusoe' was in his sixties, an unpretentious, simple man. Visually, he looked battered and tired, perhaps by the harsh environment and the uneasy lifestyle of looking after the family, as his wife appeared to be in poor health as well.

I mentioned the fact that Signor Cossu had told me about him and I had taken the liberty of visiting; I hoped he would not mind my intrusion. He was pleased to meet me and make my acquaintance, he said, welcoming me inside the house and introducing me to his family. They were almost ready to have lunch and he offered to share the meal with me. Before I had even opened my mouth, he dished out some boiled rice and a whole fish for me. It did not look very appetising as the fish looked unsavoury, and bland; it reminded me of my mum's cooking following doctor's orders for my father when he was unwell. I thanked Vargiolu politely for the generous offer but, being a fussy eater, I could not stomach the food he had served, and I excused myself by saying that I had eaten a sandwich on my way to his house.

I explained I was there just to satisfy my curiosity about our hometown connection. It transpired that he had emigrated to East Africa after a tumultuous period in Tunisia at the end of the Second World War. In Kenya, he met his wife-to-be, a Seychellois, and, when trouble occurred during the Mau-Mau Uprising, they decided to move and settle in the Seychelles. Vargiolu had never set foot on the islands before, but his wife owned this beautiful property at Anse Lazio, and it was here that they had decided to put down roots. He built the house by transporting its bricks and mortar by pirogue, stone by stone, entirely on his own. They had neither running water nor electricity and lived off vegetables produced on a little plot and Vargiolu's daily catch of fish. He rarely ventured to Mahé but occasionally made the trip to the grocery store in the local village for their basic food necessities. They lived a very isolated life next to one of the most beautiful beaches in the Seychelles.

The property was next to a large lagoon and surrounded by a unique Garden of Eden filled with exotic flora and fauna. The middle of the lagoon had a granite outcrop topped with coconut palm trees, like something from the movie set of *Treasure Island*. As the tide came in and out, the water of the lagoon was recycled continuously, which also allowed for marine life to interchange habitats.

It turned out that Vargiolu's mum was a Terralbese, and his father was Sardinian as well, but from the southeast. He was happy as we chatted in Sardinian; he had not spoken the language for years! He asked me to thank Signor Cossu for having suggested the visit and was saddened when the time came for me to leave, although I promised to return to visit him again.

My uphill journey back was even more laborious than the way in. When I got to the Moke I was completely shattered. I was covered in mosquito bites and my shirt and jeans were soaked with perspiration. Louis had been right – I was not dressed for the expedition. I caught the late afternoon flight to Mahé and could not wait to hop in the shower to cool off, wash away the sweat and apply some Tiger Balm to relieve my mosquito bites.

Chapter twenty seven

The Glitzy Party

Signor Cossu invited the Nairobi-based Italian ambassador to visit the Seychelles for a short holiday break in order to extend relations with the local government. Taking advantage of his visit, Cossu organised a dinner party at his residence so the ambassador could meet the island's Italian community. There were about 30 nationals living in the country at the time and it turned out to be one of those hot-ticket invitations one certainly would not want to miss.

Signor Cossu had a delightfully grand villa that reflected his high standard of living. It was located in the exclusive Val Riche Estate at Sans Souci, above Victoria. The residence of the Indian high commissioner, where we had celebrated the Diwali festival, was nearby. High up on the mountain slopes, the villa had a spectacular bird's-eye view over Victoria and the inner islands.

We arrived at nightfall; the entrance was lit up with white festoon lights that continued along the trees of the tropical gardens leading to the villa. The trunks of the palm trees were also dressed, adding to the dreamy setting.

The residence, following the theme, was ablaze. The open terrace, situated at the back, had a large swimming pool lit with submerged lights, the water reflecting a rainbow of glitzy colours. Table and chairs were set and placed thoughtfully around the space. Large candles were lit along its perimeter to add to the romantic ambience. As dusk fell, the glittering lights of Victoria were spread out before us. The venue was unbelievably stunning, like a Hollywood film set.

The Italian ambassador appeared, elegantly dressed in a light-blue suit and white shirt, accompanied by his wife in a long evening dress; they looked like a fashion-conscious couple. The host and hostess matched the guest of honour by wearing similarly flashy and stylish clothes. Signor Cossu loved to make a good impression, showing off his Italian eagerness, *far bella figura*.

Signora Cossu was the grand lady of the house, making sure the housekeeping ran smoothly. She clearly enjoyed living in beautiful houses managed by many servants and publicly displaying her wealth. She would often be seen in town in her chauffeur-driven car, impeccably dressed in a fashionable straw hat and creamy gloves. She maintained her gracious manners and rigid social etiquette at all times, even though they were sometimes at odds with the social environment.

Signor Cossu gave a short speech, welcoming his guests along with the ambassador, marking the beginning of the celebrations.

I mingled with new arrivals and old acquaintances. With soft background music playing, waiters served drinks and canapés, and there followed a cold buffet of Italian and international cuisine. Signor Cossu was the consummate host. 'Only he could give such a perfect party,' remarked Mr Floris as the champagne flowed. The abundance of lobster, prawns and other seafood was amazing, considering the difficulty of procuring such delicacies. No expense had been spared. It was an unbelievable treat!

The food was so well prepared and exquisite that Mr Floris could not stop complimenting the host. He was enjoying the party in a way that I had never seen him do before. 'Enjoy!' he kept saying to me. 'It is all free, Cossu is paying.' This was Signor Cossu at his best: lavish and opulent. He liked to impress and to be talked about in this way. He wanted to keep his standards high to maintain his reputation for extravagance.

The next day, at the office, Mr Floris remarked how it had certainly been the best party he had ever been to. Signor Cossu sure knew how to throw a party!

Chapter twenty eight

A Mysterious Guest, April 1978

Nicole, Signor Cossu's secretary, was a pretty Seychellois-Chinese girl. Slim and tall, she was also very bright and resourceful. She had been working for Cossu for a few years and was mainly in charge of organising his work schedule. One day, she delivered a note to the office saying that a management meeting would be held at Cossu's office at the Pirates Arms the following morning at midday. Apparently, this was the first time that he had called for a meeting of the managerial staff.

That morning, Mr Floris and I got together with Mr Perrillo, who had instructed the other four managers to gather at the Pirates Arms directly. Fritz and the whole entourage were waiting outside, although Signor Cossu had not yet arrived.

Moments later, his white chauffeur-driven car pulled in, the Italian flag clamped to the right fender. The chauffeur, a young Creole man, dressed in a freshly pressed beige shirt and trousers, white gloves and a matching hat pulled in and got out of the car, before proceeding to open the back passenger door.

Signor Cossu briskly appeared, in his colonial khaki suit, which had been tailor-made in a hotel in Hong Kong during one of his business trips. Smiling, he greeted us saying 'Buon giorno, come va? Bene?' as he walked into the foyer. It felt like it was stage-managed. Perhaps he wanted to remind us that he was the star, *the prima donna,* or he simply liked showing off his top role. Nicole opened the door and ushered him inside; she gave a big smile and looked provocative enough, in a long, tight dress, to raise an eyebrow. We all followed him inside. Signor Cossu settled down at his desk and gestured for Nicole to let us in.

He thanked us for being there and told us that a big shot was arriving on Sunday on the Somali Airlines flight from Mogadishu, politely implying that, as managers of his group of companies, our attendance at the airport for his arrival was mandatory. We ought to be on our best behaviour, with no beach shorts or flip-flops, he warned, as this person was particularly important and Cossu wanted to impress him. The so-called meeting was over in a matter of minutes. No name was mentioned and neither was the purpose of the guest's visit disclosed.

That Sunday morning, we all turned up at the airport, smartly dressed as requested to meet the mysterious guest. Signor Cossu gave a deep sigh of relief when the old Somali Boeing 720 landed on schedule, as on more than one occasion the Somali president had diverted the aircraft for state business, cancelling the weekly flight to the Seychelles.

The flight was the only aircraft landing at the airport that morning. Signor Cossu was waiting anxiously with Mr Floris and me, cracking a few jokes to clear his nerves and lighten the mood.

Blue Safari, one of Signor Cossu's companies, represented the airline in the Seychelles. Mr Perrillo personally handled its operation at the airport as station manager for the airline. Perrillo had security clearance that gave him entrance in the terminal and access to the aircraft while it was still on the tarmac. He had gone to perform his airport duties inside the terminal. Whoever this person was, it was clearly someone important. I have never seen Signor Cossu that restless, nor Mr Floris.

His chauffeur had parked the car close to the arrivals post. Two more cars were prepared, waiting for the guests. All the cars had been polished to a strong shine for the occasion. Instructions had already been given concerning which road to take and places to avoid en-route to the hotel. Everything was perfectly organised, with some help from Nicole.

Suddenly, our chitchat stopped as Signor Cossu saw his guest and entourage appear from the arrival doors with Mr Perrillo at the helm. He moved towards the party, and we followed behind. The man was in his late forties or early fifties, of short stature and muscular build, with a sun-tanned face, a wrinkled forehead and an ungroomed, greying beard that covered half of his face. He was wearing a long white tunic and an embroidered *taqiyya* cap.

His name was Giovanni Mario Ricci, but everyone addressed him as Mario Ricci. Signor Cossu welcomed him warmly; his skills of seduction, always second-to-none, went into overdrive. He kissed Mario's Ricci's wife's hand and charmed her with smooth talk; his ways had become familiar to me by now, except this time, his personality had changed. He was projecting himself as a respectful, modest man, almost submissive – a new, unrecognisable side of his character. We had not seen him behave in that fashion before.

Mr Ricci's entourage consisted of seven people. There was only one woman, his wife Angela, a lady in her late thirties with long brunette hair. She had been born in Somalia to an Italian father and Ethiopian-Eritrean mother, and had worked for the Italian embassy in Mogadishu before marrying Ricci. Ricci's younger brother, Giuseppe, was also part of the group. He was a tall, voluminous man, dressed in a beige tunic and an embroidered cap like his brother. Gianmarco Lauro was introduced as Ricci's personal secretary. The rest of his administrative staff were dressed in light western clothes, except for Gianmarco, who was wearing a navy business suit with a white shirt and no tie.

The drivers arranged to collect the guests' luggage and Signor Cossu directed them to the cars. We shook their hands and bid them *arrivederci, a domani,* 'welcome, until tomorrow'. The cars sped away towards the hotel, as instructed. Mr and Mrs Ricci got in the car with Signor Cossu and left.

We were there to attest to the strength of Signor Cossu's businesses. We were unaware of the reasons but believed we had accomplished his wishes.

Mr Floris and Mr Perrillo returned to the bungalows at Machabee together. I drove back home; Helena had arranged a picnic by the beach with friends. I spent the rest of the day guessing what all the fuss was about. Who was Ricci? What did he want? What was Cossu planning and why had he been so humble and submissive?

The following day, Ricci and Cossu met privately. Later, after lunch, Cossu met with Mr Floris and Perrillo and, to everybody's surprise, delivered the news that he had signed an agreement to transfer some of his portfolio assets to Mr Ricci. Mr Floris and Mr Perrillo had been completely unaware of this. They had been suspicious of Signor Cossu' recent behaviour, and of his connection with the mysterious Mr Ricci, but they had never imagined such a scenario. They were furious for being excluded; after all, Mr Floris was a major investor in the group and Perillo was the managing director.

Mr Ricci had not tried to negotiate on the value of the business, eagerly accepting Cossu's valuation and paying in full – at odds with the usual practice. Neither party was to know why both were so willing to complete the deal. Signor Cossu had got the best out of the transaction. Looking back with Mr Floris later, we both came to think they had had a premeditated business arrangement. The announcement initiated lots of questions, but Signor Cossu, with his charming nature and smooth talk, managed to downplay the new situation. He preferred to concentrate on upcoming projects and the company's bright future.

Signor Cossu had met Mr Ricci while on a Somali Airlines flight from Mogadishu to Rome sometime before the 1977 coup d'état in the Seychelles. The two had sat in the first-class cabin and engaged in friendly conversation. After a formal introduction and small talk, they had exchanged business cards. They had stayed in contact, and with Signor Cossu always on the lookout for new investors, he had discovered that Ricci was extraordinarily receptive to a possible future investment in the Seychelles. Neither one could believe their luck.

In the late 1960s, Italy had gone through some prosperous yet chaotic years. Mr Ricci had established a holding company registered in Switzerland under the GMR Société Anonyme, taken ownership and control of several Italian companies with links to the Social Democratic Party, and then in a matter of only a few years closed them down to bypass Italian government restrictions on diverting funds abroad. He had mysteriously become extraordinarily rich, powerful and politically well connected. He also controlled some healthy funds on behalf of anonymous investors. In 1972, he moved his business to Somalia and established a lucrative operation. A few years later, he encountered trouble with the Somali government, as his relationship with the president soured and he was asked to leave the country. So, his tumultuous years in Somalia had ended with an expulsion, as he became *persona non grata*.

Mr Ricci turned out to be an ingenious fixer. With his connections worldwide, nothing was too much trouble for him.

Chapter twenty nine

The New Co-Owner

The Ocean Gate House project was finally completed in June 1978 with President René and his cabinet ministers in attendance at the opening ceremony. We were all there; it was an opportunity for us to mingle with the president and his entourage. Mr Ricci's wife attended the ceremony alone, as apparently Mr Ricci did not socialise very much in public.

The Ocean Gate House building was located on the old pier. The three-storey construction consisted of shops, offices and apartments. After the opening, we moved our offices from the Kingsgate House to the new building.

As the new co-owner of the Ocean Gate House building, Mario Ricci settled his office HQ right next to our office. We became practically neighbours. He went on a purchasing spree with his questionably sourced, unlimited funds and purchased a beautiful villa at Glacis, overlooking the ocean, employing a famous Italian architect to completely redesign and refurbish it. He engaged SOGIS to restore the villa to the architect's specifications. I got to see him almost every day at the site or at his office in town. His staff commented on how he could be harsh and intimidating at times; Mr Ricci and his architect got into several arguments over the design of the property. The restoration of his villa took longer than expected due to the continuous changes. He ended up paying us twice as much as we had anticipated for the renovations, but he paid promptly and in full for our services. He had been an excellent client, after all.

This was the case for Signor Cossu. A few months after he settled in, Ricci discovered discrepancies in the inadequate deal he had made with Cossu. According to the company's statuary books, Cossu had sold Ricci more equity shares in the companies then were actually registered. He had deceived him; naively thinking that Ricci was ill-equipped, gullible and would not uncover this fact for some time. While he had played this game with many of his partners in the past and managed to get away unscathed, Signor Cossu was no match for Ricci. The meeting that followed was like none before. Ricci made death threats to Cossu, forcing him to reverse the shareholding position. Cossu had never been directly confronted with such peril, and was shocked and frightened by Ricci's severe reaction, finally coming to terms with his unsuccessful scheme.

After the explosive meeting, I met Ricci's personal secretary, Gianmarco, on his way to the office. He pulled me over and said to tell my boss not to 'mess' with Ricci. I relayed the message but immediately realised that it was unnecessary: Signor Cossu already understood. He subsequently asked the embassy in Nairobi for any information on Ricci. The classified information that came back was not good, allegedly linking Ricci to illicit activities. Signor Cossu had not been aware of Ricci's shady background.

Sometime after Ricci invested in the Seychelles, I met the magistrate of the town of Viareggio, on the Tuscan coast of Italy, at a dinner party one evening. After introductions and small talk, he asked me about my life in the Seychelles, and if I knew anything of Mario Ricci, who was now residing there. He divulged the fact that Ricci was an old acquaintance who had been born and grown up in the region. While in his early thirties, Ricci had been prosecuted and convicted for forgery and illegal gambling, and he was the judge who had sentenced him! The conversation turned out to be very thorny because of the topic even though the encounter was purely coincidental!

Chapter thirty

Time to Split the Group

The friendly relationship between Cossu and Floris hit a stumbling block after the secret Ricci deal; it was an eye opener for Mr Floris. Floris and I shared an office and we spent more time together than anyone else did. As time went by, I was eventually allowed to accompany him into Signor Cossu's office along with Mr Perrillo to discuss the future of the companies. In such meetings, I would normally listen and refrain from intervening unless specifically asked – which happened rarely. Once back in our office, I would express my opinion, whether asked or not. Whether we agreed or disagreed on issues, Floris and I were always frank and constructive and never acrimonious. I greatly admired him for how he conducted business, and I had the utmost respect for him as my boss and elder. The seriousness, professionalism and politeness we shared were strengths in our working relationship. He eventually confided in me more often and discussed business matters more freely. I came to feel more like part of the top managerial team, able to voice my point of view. He also appreciated my judgement of character, as I was often blunt.

Questions began to surface and Signor Cossu was not forthcoming in answering them. Funds were often moved between accounts for cashflow reasons, but the purpose of the transactions was not always clear. The movement of funds started to create mistrust between Cossu and Floris. Cossu was not pleased to be questioned and affairs got murkier. Floris, after discussing the issues with me and now fully aware of the recurring pattern of how Signor Cossu operated the entire group of businesses, confronted him. To Mr Floris's surprise, he found Signor Cossu agreeable to the idea splitting up the group of the companies.

It took a few weeks of negotiating to settle on a new roadmap. Following consultations, valuations, and accounting verifications, they agreed that the group would split into two corporations – with the airline, travel and hotel operation business headed by Cossu, and the construction, import-export and development business by Floris.

Upon further scrutiny, we realised Signor Cossu's sumptuous lifestyle had been being financed by the companies, in comparison to the modest, self-financed lifestyle of Mr Floris. Shockingly, it became apparent that SOGIS had even paid for the party at the Cossu residence during the Italian ambassador's visit. Mr Floris, therefore, had indirectly contributed to the party to remember, without any knowledge of it. Mr Floris was inconsolably furious that this publicity stunt had been at his own expense! He felt deceived and cheated by his partner and friend.

Perrillo remained to administer Cossu's part of the business and I, being Floris's personal assistant, felt it my duty to stay with him, despite the fact that it had been Signor Cossu who had originally brought me to the Seychelles.

With the new company structure, I now had to take on Perrillo's roles in helping Mr Floris deal with banking and administrative duties. I had no knowledge of the arrangements, and initially found the bank meetings frustrating and difficult to understand. Taking control of the companies was like opening a Pandora's box; it was full of surprises, revealing unexpected problems and issues!

Chapter thirty one

A Break from Paradise, July 1978

My annual leave was due, and I arranged to visit the family in Sardinia for the first time since I had left. It had been busy for months and I needed a break from paradise! I would never have thought I would need to escape, but I was happy to be spending four weeks away from work as the issues had piled up.

I booked my flight to Rome, via Nairobi, with Kenya Airways. A few days before my departure, I exchanged my local savings into dollars in preparation. I was so proud of what I had managed to save, and I was planning to gift my parents by financing part of the renovations at the house in Terralba.

The afternoon flight from Mahé landed in Nairobi as scheduled. My stopover there was several hours and I wandered around waiting for my connection, which was to depart around midnight. I made my way casually to the gate once it was announced, to find four Kenyan security guards questioning and searching any passengers with hand luggage. The officers each wielded a truncheon and had fierce, unfriendly expressions. I queued with my fellow passengers and waited my turn until one of the officers signalled with his baton for me to come forward, ordering me to empty my luggage and pockets onto the table. I complied and laid all my possessions out, including the sealed plastic envelope of five thousand dollars in cash for my parents.

His sleepy partner instantly came alive as he spied the envelope, instructing me to collect my belongings and follow him. I obeyed his demand and followed him to a small room next door with a desk with chairs and a cubicle with hanging curtains. I guessed it was a room for conducting searches.

His higher-ranking counterpart sat on the chair beside the desk, and I was asked to sit opposite him. 'Sleepy' joined us and sat on the desk facing me. In broken English, they started questioning me about the cash. I knew of the currency restrictions in Kenya and pulled out my documentation to show that I had arrived from the Seychelles and was on my way to Rome, that I had a legitimate job in the Seychelles, and supplied the bank receipt showing the transaction. But it was to no avail.

They ignored my documents and protestations and became abusive, implying that I had broken the rules of the Kenyan government and that I had met someone to obtain the dollars illegally. The accusations seemed so unreal and baseless, as I had all the paperwork to prove otherwise. *What was this all about*, I pondered. The departure time for my Rome flight was approaching, and the clock was ticking. Over the tannoy, I could hear the announcement, 'last call for flight KQ121 to Rome' and yet I remained unlawfully detained. I started to panic that I would miss my flight, along with my connection to Sardinia. Would they arrest me? I started picturing Kenyan jail cells and wondered how I could get out of this situation.

I informed the two officers that I was in danger of missing my flight and protested that they were holding me unlawfully and had better let me go. The seated officer banged his truncheon sharply on the desk and repeated his accusations. As calmly as I could, I gave him the same answer. I was petrified. Then they left me in the room alone. My name was called for departure. Time was running out.

Suddenly, they reappeared and indicated with their batons that I could go. Relief washed over me. I caught my breath, collected my loose dollars from the table to gather them into the plastic envelope, and rushed out of the room straight to the departure gate, not once looking back at my impromptu jailers.

The air hostess escorted me into the aircraft after checking my boarding pass. As I sat down, I realised how badly shaken I was. However, once inside in the plane I felt a strong sense of relief after the frightening experience. Once we had taken off, I told my story to the passenger next to me. He was an Italian expatriate, now living permanently in Uganda. On listening to my story, he politely laughed. Apparently, it was a normal occurrence at African airports. Immigration and customs officers were corrupt, and often preyed on passengers. To avoid confrontation or harassment, one had to pay them a token gift, usually some cash, a bottle of whisky or a carton of cigarettes. He smirked at my naivety.

* * *

My eldest brother Bruno picked me up from Cagliari airport. My return was quite the event, not because I had been gone for long, as I had lived in England for much longer before, but because I was returning from such a remote and unknown country. The recent events that had engulfed the Seychelles also had my family worried and uneasy, and it had been exceedingly difficult to communicate with them. Letters took up to four weeks to arrive and telephone calls were expensive with frustratingly patchy connections. As challenging as it was for me to get a clear, undisturbed line, my parents had no telephone in the house and had to arrange in advance for an appointment to call from the public booths at the telephone office near the piazza.

Once I was home, I found my whole family gathered to welcome me back. I felt like the prodigal son. They could not wait to hear about my new life in the Seychelles. Mama organised a special Sunday lunch, a treat reserved only for big occasions, which my brothers and their families were to attend. She got up at dawn and, with the kitchen in full swing, she prepared, baked and cooked. She even lit the barbeque and grilled my favourite *melanzane*, aubergine, with her special parsley and garlic sauce. She set up the long table reserved for long family banquets on the veranda. At precisely one o'clock, she dished out a delicious spread of *antipasti*, followed by lasagne, roasted piglet, sausages with roasted potatoes, grilled aubergine and peppers, celery sticks, radishes and slides of bread scattered around, the tablecloth. Dessert was a choice of crème caramel or tiramisu. As it was July, Babbu cut everyone huge slices of watermelon and honey dew melon, signifying the end of the meal that had lasted until five o'clock.

While we indulged in my mother's cooking, I sated their curiosity. I had to water down facts and omit some events so that I would not make my parents any more worried than they already were. They admired my tenacity. I felt so proud of their display of affection towards me.

I had brought back a bag of exotic fruit with mangoes, papayas, avocados, pineapple, rare red and mignon bananas, and coconuts. They had never even heard of most of these fruits with exception of the bananas and pineapple. I also brought spices, including yellow saffron, garam masala, chilli, curry powder, vanilla pods, cinnamon sticks and nutmeg. I showed them the beautiful, colourful seashells that I had picked up on the reefs. I felt like I was Marco Polo returning from his travels with a bounty of exotic ingredients and treasures.

This led to an introductory lesson and tasting of the strange fruit. Naturally, some were less appreciated than others were; however, my brothers and sisters-in law were more enthusiastic, as they were more open-minded. However critical he was, it felt good that my father at least tried to taste some of the tropical fruit. Underneath the criticism, he was immensely proud of me; his actions proved more than words could speak. At the piazza, he spoke non-stop of my achievements and my life in the Seychelles to his friends.

When I was alone with Mama, she asked me to tell her more of my stories. Keeping my promise, I told her about my experiences of life on the islands and how the Seychellois lived. She was fascinated by different cultures and customs and wanted to know more. The only external contact she had with the rest of the world was through the TV soap operas and movies. I showed her some photographs that I had taken. With her innate mother's instinct, she picked out Helena in the pictures and asked who she was. I hesitated, not yet sure of the seriousness of our relationship, and said that she was my maid who looked after the house! Mama was pleased. She said she looked like a nice person.

On my departure, she baked *amaretti* almond cakes to take with me. She prepared a separate parcel for 'the maid' to thank her for looking after her son! Before leaving, I arranged to have a telephone installed in the house so that we could keep in better touch.

The journey back was uneventful. Kenya Airways operated the Seychelles route after East Africa Airways went bust. The aircraft used on these routes were old, second-hand jets on wet lease from British Midland Airways, who also provided maintenance of the planes. Somehow, they managed to run on schedule most of the time!

Descending into Mahé was quite special. I could now name all the islands I saw from my plane window. I had no trouble with immigration, as I was now a resident with a work permit.

Helena picked me up; I had not seen her for a month. As we kissed and embraced, I found myself aroused, it was intense. She felt it and looked at me with desire in her eyes. We had attracted the attention of a few onlookers, some of Helena's friends and colleagues at the airport. A couple of girls and a boy nearby giggled with squeaky laughter, mouthing, and signalling to each other, 'look at his bulge, wow.' There was nothing we could do to help the situation and got in the car horny as hell. It was a crazy and beautiful feeling, but as she was still working, and we could not fulfil our desires until later that evening.

After travelling for almost 24 hours, I felt very tired, as I had not managed to sleep on the plane. I had to remain alive and not succumb to fatigue. I took a cool shower followed by an early dinner with dessert after. Afterwards, we made passionate love and reached orgasm together. The long abstinence had only created a bigger desire. With my senses and sex-drive satisfied, and my body relaxed and overcome by the fatigue, we fell soundly asleep until the next morning.

Chapter thirty two

East Africa Adventure, Christmas 1978

It had been a very chaotic and busy few months since my return from Sardinia; the work just kept piling up. Floris and I tirelessly worked long hours to get things done. We were not in danger of burning out, but the news that Floris would be travelling to Sardinia for the Christmas holidays was welcome, as it meant I could take things a little easier for a while.

Helena and I decided to take a trip to East Africa to visit Kenya, Malawi and Tanzania for the New Year. Nick and Anne planned to join as far as Kenya, where they would stay behind for a safari and to visit friends. We flew to Nairobi on Kenya Airways and stayed at the New Stanley Hotel there. Two days later, an old Air Malawi Bac 1-11 jet flew us to Blantyre, in Malawi where we stayed at the delightful Mount Soche Hotel. Close to the city centre, the hotel was surrounded by beautiful, lush tropical gardens.

Malawi was quite an intriguing place. The president, Dr Banda, had a conservative approach to running the country. To obtain visas, men were not allowed to have beards or long hair. For women, skirts had to be a minimum of knee-length and low-neckline tops were forbidden. In order to rent a car, the driver was required to sign a clause stating that, if we were to encounter the president's motorcade, we must stop, exit the car and wave happily. I thought these rules were odd, but I had to respect them. The bizarre head of state had declared himself 'President for Life' and had become the most totalitarian ruler in Africa. His power was absolute; no decision was taken in the country without his consent. In public, Dr Banda was always seen dressed in a dark three-piece suit. Nearly all the local men wore smart jackets and ties, like a uniform, a style they adopted to give the impression of a country of equality.

Blantyre city's pavements were full of tailors busy with their sewing machines. The countryside looked immaculate with neatly cultivated fields. Everyone was so friendly – the country of smiling faces, exactly as advertised.

Three days later, a British Airways flight B707 took us to Dar es Salaam. It was late when we arrived, and we took a taxi straight to the Kilimanjaro Hotel, as I had heard it was the best in town. We had no reservation, and we discovered the place was fully booked. It turned out all the other hotels in Dar es Salaam were sold out as well. Because of the New Year festivities, the only room we managed to find available was at the Hotel Skyways. The hotel foyer looked untidy, unclean and not very inviting. Only one room was available, and another English couple was there to take it if we declined. They asked us to pay before we even had the chance to see it.

We got our luggage into the filthy lift. As we entered our bedroom, our mood did not improve. The bed-frame was rusty, the bedsheets had holes, and the shower was dirty and in a bad state of repair. Helena sat on a corner of the bed and tears began to run down her cheeks. We could not spend the night there.

We were so disappointed by the state of room that we decided to find a hotel outside the city. Using the telephone in the room, I made several calls before I found one available by the beach, some 200 miles north of the city, on an unpaved road. The taxi cost as much as the hotel room we had just paid for. We drove all night and arrived at the beach hotel in the early hours of the morning. We had a basic room but at least it was clean. The main reason for the trip to Tanzania was to experience the city of Dar es Salaam and its Arabic-German-British heritage, but due to the circumstances and our location, it became impossible. We decided to stay put and enjoy the resort. At least Helena found her favourite dessert on the menu, generously helping herself to the chef's crème caramel for the two nights we were there. Then we gladly embarked the Air Tanzania Boeing 737 and safely returned to Mahé.

Chapter thirty three

A Resourceful Lady

The illegitimate daughter of a rich landowner with an impressive estate who owned properties throughout the St Louis area up to Beau Vallon beach, Helena's mum, Helen, was quite the character. Upon the landowner's death, Helen's half-sister, Hilda, his only legitimate child, inherited everything. Out of love for her half-sister, Hilda had gifted Helena's mother a large plot of property in St Louis.

Madame Morel, or Mere, as we called Helena's mother, lived alone in a colonial-style house built entirely from local wood. It was raised from the ground to protect from floods and insects, and it had a high-pitched shingle roof to shield it from the heavy rains. I found the house a bit spooky, as it had an aura of mystery, but it was in an attractive setting.

The main building housed the bedrooms and a living room. It was connected to the kitchen, dining room and bathroom by a few open-air corridors, each leading to a separate room. The main building was surrounded by wide verandas, protected by curtains of thinly split strips of bamboo to attenuate the sunlight or rain, creating the communal space. The house was cooled by natural ventilation. French windows, with draught spaces at both the top and bottom, gave access to the rooms and allowed air to circulate. The wooden floors were clean and shining, as the maid brushed them daily with half a coconut husk. The courtyard and flowering gardens were always kept clean and shaded.

Helena told me that her Mum had very peculiar ways. A practising Christian and an avid churchgoer, she also believed in a sort of witchcraft named *gris-gris*. Seychellois were devout believers in the afterlife and feared evil spirits. Envy and jealousy were the main culprits, and a visit to *Bonom di bwa* (literally 'goodman of the woods' but usually a woman who practised traditional medicine) was necessary to ward off the evil eye. Madame Morel often visited an old medicine woman known as Madame Antoine, who lived in the woods above her estate. Her mum consulted her for health problems or worries of any nature; after each visit, Madame Antoine would deliver her findings in the form of recipes for herbal remedies or spiritual advice after consulting with death in her sleep. Helena said that, sometimes, if she were short of cash, her mum would pay Madame Antoine with an ornament, such as a piece of brass from the house.

It reminded me of my mum's flowerpots at home. She had needles poked in the leaves to reject the evil eye of jealous visitors. My schoolfriend's mother also practiced cleansings from *malocchio*, evil spirits who possessed babies and small children. She would immerse her St Christopher's medallion in a glass of water; if bubbles formed around the face of the saint, the victim was indeed affected by the *malocchio*. She would then recite some prayers and wash the victim's face with the same water to remove the evil spirit.

When visiting Madame Morel, I used the back door, as she was often in the rear kitchen. One day I saw the main entrance door half-open, and, thinking she was home, I entered the house, calling her name. I entered the living room and, as I walked in, I encountered a wooden coffin. I jumped, frightened by the sight. I felt my pulse quicken and blood pressure rising, was I about to have a heart attack? As I was trying to understand what was happening, Madame Morel entered. She was composed and calm, and asked me why I looked so pale and fearful. What was the matter? I gasped for air and, once I managed to catch my breath, I told her that I was not used to seeing a coffin in the living room. She said she had got it just in case. Her explanation freaked me out.

A week later, the coffin in her living room disappeared, I thought she might have moved it to a more discreet location. To avoid any more surprises, I dared to ask her of its whereabouts. She said she had lent it to an acquaintance, who required it urgently. In time, she would exchange it for a new one.

Madame Morel had some unusual pets: giant tortoises. The creatures were over 100 years old and were free to roam in a large, fenced area of the garden. When it was mating season, the male would ram into the female, usually during the midday heat. The whole affair was slow, enduring and noisy. Excruciating hissing and grunting sounds could be heard resounding throughout the whole estate.

Madame Morel was a very resourceful lady. To supplement her income, she sold coconuts from a property in Beau Vallon, eggs from her hens, home-made tobacco to chew, and *kalou*, the natural juice of the toddy palm, which, once fermented, turns into alcohol. The locals loved it. To regulate consumption, authorities registered each tree, writing numbers on their trunks and requiring their owners to pay a licence fee.

Chapter thirty four

The House at St Louis

Madame Morel grew to like me. One day, out of the blue, she suggested that Helena and I move into the empty house down at the bottom of the estate, which belonged to Helena but was in desperate need of repair. The detached house had been left neglected for a while; it had an overgrown garden with palm trees and a variety of strikingly coloured flowers such as hibiscus, flamingo lily, bird of paradise and red alpine. At the back of the house, there was a grove of banana trees of all shapes and sizes. We decided to take her up on her offer.

I redesigned the interior to breathe life back into the property, adding extra features to make it our own. I organised a small team of workmen from the Point Conan workshop to tend to all the repairs and refurbishments. Another team was called in to landscape the gardens and, within a few weeks, we moved in.

We were pleasantly surprised with the results. We had built a curved seating area for the dining table from stone and mortar, with customised pillows to make it cosy. The dining area and living room were on a split-level, with flooring made from reconditioned hardwood that we managed to save from the property. We also had a bar that was built entirely from local wood for entertaining our guests at parties. The house was halfway between town and the beach at Beau Vallon, making for an easy ride to the office.

Helena had a new job, managing a small self-catering resort at Mare Anglaise, just beyond Beau Vallon. The English-owned Vacoa Village was a charming Andalusian-style property perched on granite rocks overlooking the sea. Its whitewashed cottages blended in beautifully with the surrounding nature and the vibrant planted hibiscus and bougainvillea. Complementing the location was a stunning swimming pool surrounded by a green lawn and a rustic bar.

If we were not too busy at lunchtime, Helena and I would rendezvous at home for a snack and a bit of fun, often racing to the bedroom for snatched moments of pleasure.

Being our neighbour, Madame Morel also appreciated my Italian cooking. Pasta and minestrone were her favourites. She was also a great cook; my very favourite dishes were her creamy and tender octopus curry with coconut milk and her braised beef, slow cooked for hours in the traditional Creole way, in a cast iron la marmite pot on open fire. She often cooked breadfruit chips for me, *frya pen,* as Seychellois believed that guests who eat the fruit will always return to the islands.

One day at our house, we noticed problems with our toilet. Most likely, our septic tank was full, as we had no mains sewage system. Madame Morel planned for two of her occasional workers to empty the septic tank. Early the next morning, before going to work, Helena and I stayed behind to supervise. The men proceeded to remove the cover of the overflowing tank. Amongst the human waste, we noticed what looked like hundreds of multicoloured rubber bags floating on the surface. Helena and I were stunned by the sight and helplessly looked at each other, speechless and horribly embarrassed, struggling to find the words to smooth over the situation. Suddenly Madame Morel spoke in Creole, '*ki sis sa, eh*?' What is that? What were those balloons doing there? I bet the kids have thrown them into the toilet, she said, referring to her granddaughter's recent birthday party where there had been balloons galore. She showed such innocence and naivety. She had no idea that they were condoms and that Helena, and I regularly threw them down the toilet. We kept our mouths shut and nodded, agreeing with her assumptions. If the men knew what had blocked the toilet, they did not betray us in front of Madame Morel. We let them proceed with the job in hand and went our separate ways to work.

While living at the house in St Louis, some friends suggested we adopt a dog since we had a large garden. Due to our working commitments and neither of us having owned one before, we were unsure of the idea. However, one evening, our friends unexpectedly arrived at the house with a puppy. He was cute but looked rather sad; '*I fer lapen*', Helena said, expressing pity. He was a typical Seychellois dog, a mixed breed with a similar stature to an Alsatian. We decided to keep him and built a kennel on our large, covered veranda. We named him Laika, after the first Russian dog who went to space. Laika had his own character and a natural guard-dog instinct but was not too serious or diligent in keeping up with his duties. Quiet and playful, he loved the outdoors; he always enthusiastically hopped into the back seat of the Mini Moke for a ride to the beach. Laika was an avid fish-eater. All dogs in the Seychelles enjoyed a home-cooked diet of fish and rice. He was an expert in leaving the entire shining skeleton of a red snapper intact after stripping away all the meat!

Chapter thirty five

In Charge of Operations, February 1979

Mr Floris's long-time partner in Sardinia died suddenly of a heart attack while playing tennis. His sad, unexpected death necessitated a dramatic restructuring of Floris's business responsibilities and priorities.

Eventually, Mr Floris decided to concentrate his attention on his business in Sardinia. He appointed me in general manager and director of the group of companies in the Seychelles, on the basis he would visit from time to time when necessary. I was flattered, but I did not yet have enough business experience to manage such an operation on my own. I felt too young and inexperienced.

Surely Nick was a more suitable candidate for the job, I pleaded with Mr Floris in vain, but he had made up his mind and insisted that I was the only one he could trust. My lack of experience was compensated for by the frankness and diligence that I had demonstrated during our time together.

I was so taken by the confidence he expressed in me that I accepted this new challenge; these were unforeseen circumstances, after all. Mr Floris thought I was ready and therefore I had no reason to doubt myself.

At the office, my secretary, Labonté, was delighted to hear of my promotion but was concerned about how the managerial staff would take Mr Floris's decision. They had all worked there longer and had much more experience than I did. Labonté had worked at SOGIS for a few years before I joined the company. He had a double role as a bookkeeper and a secretary, running my office diary.

He liked to gossip; he was our outlet for *radio bambou*; if I fed him news, you could be certain it would spread fast within his circle of friends. Labonté was a temperamental chap, but a good soul. He had been born in the Seychelles and moved with his family to East Africa, later working in Malawi before returning to the Seychelles. My Christmas trip to Malawi had been inspired by the fascinating tales Labonté had told me about the years he had spent in the country. He was in his thirties, married to an Italian woman, whom he had met in East Africa, and they had two teenage daughters. He had tightly curled reddish-brown hair and freckled, fair skin. His sister was a former Miss Seychelles and his brother-in-law had disappeared, presumed dead, one of the casualties of the 'bloodless' coup.

Politically, he was opposed to the René government and his wife often had to restrain him when he badmouthed the regime with strangers. He considered himself an educated man, therefore middle-class. He was Roman Catholic but, like Madame Morel and so many other Seychellois, he was also a believer in *gris-gris*. He was a reliable, honest worker and we got along quite well.

After a spell of feeling unwell and absent-minded at work, Labonté suspected that someone had cursed him with the evil eye, as they were envious of his good fortune. I laughed at him, but he was serious and a firm believer in witchcraft who turned to *Bonom di bwa* to resolve his troubles. At night, he visited his *Bonom di bwa* at a remote house in the woods of Forest Noir. The woman confirmed his curse with a bunch of chicken bones and pebbles. He was told to return the following night with a bottle of his own urine and a piece of pork. He stripped naked, then she anointed his body with his urine, using the piece of pork to rub it into his skin, all the while reciting incantations. Once dressed, he returned home and was warned not to shower until the morning. He must have stunk like a public toilet all night. Nevertheless, Labonté believed that it worked and that the evil spirit was exorcised after a deep, cleansing shower.

When Mr Floris embarked on his flight to Rome, leaving me in charge, I felt in a bit lost. He would no longer be there for advice, and I realised I had to get a better grip of my new reality. I had to become my own man.

So far, Nick and I had maintained a good business relationship, but my promotion did not go down well with him. He was displeased at having to take orders from an unexperienced junior. Empathising with his frustration, I proactively got him involved in technical decisions because of his expertise, agreeing with him most of the time, and making collaborative decisions as a team. I called regular meetings, explaining the way forward and thanking the team for their continuing support. Labonté was surprised by my skills of persuasion. My actions eventually won them over, and smoothed over the tension.

I remained ever vigilant for any trouble at the construction sites. A little trouble became part of the normal routine and I quickly learned that at times I needed to ignore the team in order to focus on bigger issues.

Chapter thirty six

The Birthday

It was my birthday and Helena had organised a party by the pool at Vacoa Village. She invited a small, well-chosen group of friends.

This was my very first birthday party in the Seychelles, such a pleasant surprise, and an occasion that I wanted to savour in full. The garden space that surrounded the open-air swimming pool was beautiful; it included a glamorous, slick-looking bar made from half a takamaka trunk that had been embedded into local granite. Helena had ordered a selection of Creole-style finger food, which was unusual considering the crowd of mostly Italian guests who were notoriously culinary unadventurous like myself, but it was very well received by all.

Lidia and Renzo Appiani joined us, they lived just by the entrance of the Vacoa Village estate. They had a beautiful, stylish villa in harmony with the rest of the village's Andalusian style. They had arrived in the Seychelles in late 1975 and decided to invest, acquiring a small hotel on Praslin. Renzo, being an artist, had turned the property into a charming boutique hotel called the Village du Pecheur.

Soon he realised that the hotelier business was not his true vocation. That realisation, combined with the quietness of the island, became too much for them and they decided to rent out the property and move to Mahé to continue Renzo's career as an artist instead.

Renzo was well-connected politically; he personally befriended Jacques Hodoul, a lawyer by profession and newly appointed minister of education and culture. According to *radio bambou,* Hodoul was the most ideological member of the René's party.

After the coup d'état, Renzo helped design the new Seychelles flag and was also commissioned to design the monument at the Independence Avenue roundabout. He created a three-winged structure that symbolised the three continents of Africa, Europe, and Asia: the origins of the Seychellois. At my party, he gifted me one of his paintings. It was ironically signed, 'On the occasion of your 18th birthday.'

The sunset at the end of the evening was breath-taking. We were located on high ground with the view towards the sea completely unobstructed. Some palm trees contributed to the perfect picture, their silhouettes majestically contouring the images. It was so beautiful that it inspired Renzo to take out his camera to shoot the whole event. The reflection of the sky in the calm sea was astonishing. Later that month, Renzo organised an exhibition of the event at a local gallery and Helena and I attended. He had turned our memory of the evening into so many beautiful images.

Chapter thirty seven

Air Seychelles

There were two airlines operating domestically between the islands' airstrips, Air Mahé and Inter-Island Airways.

Air Mahé had been in operation since 1972, when the international airport first opened. The airline was established and run by two Englishmen, Captain John Faulkner Taylor, and 'daredevil' Lieutenant Commander Tony Bentley-Buckle. They began with a single Piper PA-31 Navajo, until two Britten-Norman Islander planes replaced the Piper after the business quickly expanded.

In 1975, Signor Cossu formed his own domestic airline, Inter-Island Airways, to compete with the established Air Mahé. He started operations with a second-hand Cessna 172 and a Piper Seneca twin-engine six-seater. Signor Cossu had foreseen the growth of tourism in the Seychelles, projecting that the traffic between Mahé and Praslin would grow exponentially along with his investment in Praslin. As the tourist numbers increased and the airline got busier, he expanded his fleet and purchased two of the Britten-Norman Islander planes, which seated nine passengers and a Trislander three-engine aircraft that seated 18. Business continued to flourish.

After the coup d'état, Signor Cossu was somehow warned of the government's intentions to nationalise the airline sector, something that had been planned for quite some time but had been delayed; he had been hoping that it would not come to fruition. He worried that the government would acquire only one of the two operating airlines, forcing the other out of the business.

Because of the uncertainty about what might happen, Signor Cossu hatched a plan in agreement with the owners of Air Mahé to merge the two airlines into one holding company. By doing this, they gave the government no choice but to acquire the newly created company. It was perfectly planned and successfully executed; his strategy had worked. Air Seychelles was born in early 1979 as a new corporate entity.

It could have been that his was one of the first companies to be nationalised or perhaps it was due to a lack of experience from the government negotiators, but nevertheless the well-documented valuation of the company was paid at full value and in cash. Signor Cossu had pulled off a successful, rewarding business deal. Mr Floris and I had to attend to the sign-off of the deal, as the company books still showed Floris as director of Inter Island Airlines, due to the informal internal agreement when they split up Signor Cossu's companies.

When they began to dispose of and split Cossu's businesses, I was especially disappointed because I had admired his business achievements on the island. This would also cause dire consequences for the lives of expatriate managers like Perrillo, the general manager of the group, who I looked up to. The sale of Inter-Island Airways was the final nail in the coffin. Perillo was un-ceremonially sacked. He sadly had no other alternative but to leave the Seychelles; years of planning gone to waste. Perrillo and his young family were devastated. Signor Cossu had promised Perrillo the moon and the stars, but circumstances turned those promises into nothing. Perrillo was left only with resentment and bitterness. After his departure, I wondered if I would get the same treatment too, once my services were no longer required.

Chapter thirty eight

Underground Resistance

Initially, René's government appeared to be popular. However, the regime was beginning to cause bitterness among the upper and middle classes, as the censorship of the media and the curtailment of freedom of speech became wildly unpopular.

About a year after the coup, an underground resistance movement emerged named the Mouvement Pour La Resistance, MPR, and a regular leaflet – *Regar* – appeared widely distributed. *Regar* encouraged people to fight against the regime, with the aim of a popular uprising. René felt threatened by the secretive opposition and ordered the militia to round up all known individuals who spoke out against his regime and incarcerate them.

It turned out that one of the leaders of the MPR was Gerald Hoarau, the government's chief immigration officer. He was arrested and imprisoned in solitary confinement. Hoarau had secretly become a political activist, a subversive! Never underestimate a discreet, quiet man.

Mario Ricci had secretly supported Hoarau's cause by inconspicuously funding it. Ricci had befriended Hoarau as soon as he set foot in the country. Their friendship/business relationship had rapidly developed as Ricci had found Hoarau to be his perfect interlocutor, he spoke little English and Hoarau spoke fluent Italian. They seemed to have found common ground and Ricci actively started to sponsor his football club before moving on to support Hoarau's political ambitions.

'Enemies of the state' were kept in poor conditions at the Union Vale prison, deprived of any rights or a fair trial. After many months, exhausted and in poor health, they were given the choice of being permanently exiled from the country or remaining in prison for the foreseeable future. Hoarau decided on exile in South Africa.

Government spies and informers were everywhere; soldiers and local militia patrolled the streets creating fear. René wanted to show everyone that his power was absolute. The harmonious relationships among the Seychellois changed. The Seychellois started feel afraid and unsafe to speak their minds as rumours and *kankan* spread fast.

As the regime became more entrenched and undeterred, René continued to implement his so-called socialist programme, grabbing land from wealthy white landlords, the *gran blan*, who opposed his government. He would turn companies deemed to be of national interest into state-owned and parastatal organisations run by his cronies. The government revoked merchants import licences and created its own parastatal company to import all goods. It also imposed currency control and more regulation restrictions, eroding liberties, movement, and freedom of speech. This was all part of René's ideology of reform and his drive to abolish elitism in the country. But the cost of implementing these changes was colossal and quickly drained the treasure coffers. The country, after few years, eventually was on its knees. Those Seychellois who could afford to leave did so. Some say that between 1977 and 1990, nearly 10,000 people fled the islands.

These measures and the continued state of alert, along with the loss of liberties, gravely impacted the general public's mood. Their carefree attitude had gone, and people were scared to go to town or socialise. It was like they were all deep in a depression.

It had an impact on tourism, as well. The hostesses and representatives who met arriving guests had lost their *joie de vivre*. It was Sue, Guy's girlfriend, working as PR office for the Ministry of Tourism who conceived of and implemented the 'happy faces' advertising campaign to remind the population that the Seychelles was a tourist destination and that smiling faces went a long way towards satisfying visitors.

Chapter thirty nine

The Bigarade Island, Easter 1979

Helena and I took a small trip over Easter to the island of Felicité. It was a private island, but we knew the owner's daughter, Marie Helen, as she worked at Blue Safari. She happily allowed us to spend our Easter break there. Felicité is close to La Digue, but it was easier for us to fly to Praslin and then take a boat over.

The island's plantation had been abandoned and the manager and his family were the only remaining residents. We disembarked onto a small, derelict pier. The middle-aged Creole manager, André, welcomed us and showed us to our freshly prepared accommodation. The guest room consisted of a hexagonal unit built on a raised platform surrounded by an open veranda. The roof was made of shingles and covered with palm leaves and there were two small shutter windows facing each other for ventilation, as well a small shower room. The dwelling was quite run down but simply furnished. Marie Helen had told us in advance of the state of things, and we were not expecting anything much. After all, we were only staying there for only three nights.

Inland, nature was quite harsh and looked impervious. A forest of wild, thorny, citrus trees – the *bigarade*, a cross between lemon and bergamot orange – had literally invaded part of the island. The tree bore a tiny, round, green fruit, intensely fragrant with a bitter taste. Locally, it was served as a juice with water, sugar and a pinch of salt, deliciously refreshing and thirst-quenching.

We decided not to venture out and to stay put on the beach side. The coral on the beach was unusually sharp, and walking barefoot was not pleasurable. I had brought a mask and snorkel to explore the underwater life around the island.

It was a wonderful day, like always. The ocean was calm and serene and, as it was low tide, the reef was just meters away from our hut on the harsh coral beach, the shallowest part of it being directly attached to the shore. The waves were crashing onto the reef, which remained just below the waterline. With my mask and snorkel on, I dived into the crystal clear, warm tropical waters and was instantly gobsmacked.

The reef extended for only about 100 meters and the depth of the ocean was no more than three meters. The reef wall was flourishing, with colonies of coral in dozens of different shades and forms. The dominant brown and golden ochre colours of the Maze and Brain corals alternated with scarlet and turmeric Mushroom corals, like huge, opened umbrellas. On one side, grouped into a plateau, was a field of Pillar and Staghorn corals with their bright, soft light browns and white tipped orange colours. A huge, fluorescent coral attracted my attention with its vivid, translucent and fascinating display. Nearby, a giant clam opened, displaying its mantle tissue of deep blue, outlined with black.

All around, under and between the corals, I saw shoals of multi-coloured fish going about their day. As I got closer to the corals, I seemed to create havoc among the residents. Most of them are territorial and battle to defend their homes. I observed every creature's personal survival strategy, the bigger fishes bullying the small ones. Some had developed ingenious adaptations to survive the crowded reef, such as hiding in smaller caves or camouflaging themselves among rocks or seaweed.

I managed to distinguish some of the few species I knew – surgeon fish, triggerfish, parrot fish and angelfish, to name a few. They all exhibited dazzling, bizarre colours and patterns. The clown triggerfish changed to darker colours when it felt threatened, returning to its vivid brightness as it swam away. The black and white three-striped damselfish erected its dorsal spines to defend its space.

Upon seeing me, a manta ray shook itself free from its sandy seabed cover, and a giant moray emerged from a rocky hiding place, brandishing its ferocious dentures. A solitaire black and white sea snake, perhaps moving from one den to another, crossed my path and for a moment gave me a fright, interrupting my tranquil state. Long, slim, silver barracudas were on standby, giving me the side-eye, swimming along the edge of the reef, ready to strike their prey at the first opportunity.

Along the seaweed-blanketed seabed, I saw some large cone shells and a beautiful tiger cowrie shell grazing peacefully. I was tempted to retrieve it, as it would have been a good addition to my collection, but decided against it, as I did not have any protective gloves or a stick to check for any poisonous stonefish that could be camouflaged in the rocks.

The corals were living animals, breathing and feeding on the plankton, microscopic organisms that float with the water current. They rumbled with clicks and clacks that filled the water with constant noise, like some sort of Morse code. The fish were busy snapping or bubbling, out of tune with the rowdy, busy reef.

Trumpet fish swam straight towards me and then stopped abruptly, before swimming back and forth like gracious ballerinas at their stage debut. Their big bright, wide-open eyes displayed the weirdest curiosity towards me. Obviously, I was the alien here, the odd one out in their fascinating marine world.

André's teenage son, Pierre, asked me to join him one night to snorkel for lobsters. It sounded like an interesting proposition, as I had never done anything like that before. André had an expert knowledge of these waters, and was also a strong swimmer, which was unusual for the Seychellois.

We swam along the rocks beside the old pier. It was a less busy environment than my reef experience earlier that day. In the pitch black of the night, most of the sea creatures seemed to be in sleep mode in their designated 'bedrooms.' Pierre caught two napping lobsters, after spotting their antennas sticking out from their hiding den by the rocks. I was too busy being fascinated by the nature around me to be a useful hunting partner.

A placid sea turtle crossed our path. Pierre quickly got hold of it, rode on it, and then brought it ashore. Upon measuring its shell with his hand, he realised it was just short of the legal requirement for catching turtles and let the turtle back into the ocean.

The following day I went handline fishing in a small boat with André and Pierre. We anchored the boat facing Ile Coco, a small granite islet off Felicité. The two isles were separated by a stretch of water with a strong current where fish gathered to feed. It was a frisky, busy fishing ground, I was told. We used lines and caught an incredible amount of sizeable *job,* a sea bass-like fish. It was insane; I had never experienced such a catch in my life. As soon as the line was thrown in the water with its bait attached to the hook, a fish would be caught within minutes, pulled into the boat and thrown back. The sea was full of marine life, with fish everywhere; it was unlike anything I had ever seen before.

That night, we relaxed by the light of gas lanterns and an open fire. We barbequed our fish and the two lobsters for dinner, listening to André's stories that had been passed down by generations of past island residents. The most notorious and fascinating one was about the Sultan Abduallah of Perak, who had been accused of assassinating James Birch, the British governor of Perak. He had been exiled from Malaysia by the British as a political detainee in 1877. After a few years in Victoria, he and his family were relocated to Felicité. Far away from the luxuries of his former life, he was made to endure a basic existence on this island for five years before returning to Victoria. After being pardoned after 17 years in exile for a crime he never committed, he was finally allowed to return to his native home. On reflection, this intriguing sad story was a typical example of the darker side of life during colonial times that lurked beyond the white, sandy beaches and tropical sunshine.

Chapter forty

Welcome Elixir, July 1979

The frustrations caused by the uncertainty of the business's future, combined with the government's oppressive policies was exhausting; it had been a particularly difficult time for me. My annual holiday leave was a welcome elixir; I needed to escape and recharge. Mr Floris returned to relieve me during my month-long break, arriving a week early to familiarise himself with the latest progress on our current projects.

I was ready to leave. Helena dropped me at the airport for my late afternoon flight to Nairobi.

The Kenya Airways B707 taxied to the end of the runway and promptly fired up its four-engine jets, releasing its brakes, allowing the aircraft to propel itself forward. Seated by a window, I noticed that I was next to a group of British Airways crew, probably being transported to Nairobi on their way back to London.

As the Boeing started, the engines were given extra power to reach full throttle. We were halfway down the runway when a huge blast of noise filled the cabin. I instantly looked outside my window and saw a flashing light, giving me the impression that the engine was on fire. Quickly, I turned to watch the behaviour of the British Airways crew. They had not moved, but at the same time there was a second, more violent boom from the engines, a reverse engine blast.

All the passengers began to panic, hysterically screaming. The aircraft violently terminated its run and the force of this action was terrifying. The framework of the airplane trembled so intensely, it was as if it was breaking into pieces. The captain addressed us over the speaker, asking us to calm down announcing, 'We have had a burst tyre. Sorry for the inconvenience and the scare.' Luckily, he had managed to stop the aircraft just in time before its no return point of take-off; he had had no choice but to act the way he did.

We returned to the terminal and disembarked. Passengers and cargo were unloaded to lighten the plane and the mechanics manually replaced the busted tyres. It took them several hours to fully reload but eventually we departed the Seychelles. My connection at Nairobi was not disrupted by the late departure and there were no other delays in reaching Italy.

My holiday in Sardinia went smoothly. I loved the weather, the beach and the evening meals with friends and relatives, and most of all the company of my family. They all made a huge effort to treat me with their home-cooked meals.

I had no communication with the Seychelles during my stay in Sardinia. And that was somehow pleasing! After four weeks fully energised and at peace, I was ready to return to my now troubled islands. When I landed back in the Seychelles, I felt quite emotional and happy to be back. I felt like I was finally truly at home.

Chapter forty one

Manipulation

At the office on Monday morning, I learned that, while I was away, Mr Floris had employed Franco Esposito, our Italian air-conditioning subcontractor for Ocean Gate House. He had begged Mr Floris for a job as he did not want to return to Italy. It turned out that he had been declared bankrupt in Italy and therefore wanted to settle in the Seychelles. Mr Floris had also fired Nick, which disturbed me as I had relied so much on his expertise and technical knowledge.

Nick was fired for allegedly diverting resources and manpower from the resort-building site on Praslin to construction at the grand colonial villa belonging to Signor Cossu. On a site visit, Esposito had found out about the construction, questioned the operation, and then duly reported back to Mr Floris. Nick had failed to explain, and above all, to account for the costs. I could not imagine why.

Without a job and a sponsor, a few months after this, Nick had no alternative but to leave the Seychelles for good. Anne resented the situation and held me responsible. She decided she no longer wanted any friendship with me. As we were neighbours, she had to go past our house every day. It was incredibly difficult for Helena not to be able to speak to her own sister.

Signor Cossu continued building his colonial villa using SOGIS infrastructure without informing us, despite the fact that Mr Floris was technically the new owner. Signor Cossu's behaviour towards his staff was like a vassalage; he was terribly imposing and overbearing. He made sure that nobody dared question his demands. In his eyes, he never stopped owning his companies, even after he had sold them. People often fell for his false pretences and perhaps this time Nick had been the latest victim of his manipulation. It was too late for me to interfere as Mr Floris had already taken irrevocable steps toward his dismissal. I missed having Nick on our team, professionally and as a friend. I did not like Esposito's way of doing things. Fortunately, his employment with us turned out to be temporary and he soon moved on.

We eventually settled costs for the construction with Signor Cossu amicably. A few months later, after completion, the villa was sold to a consortium of three wealthy dentistry professionals from Bologna. Signor Cossu was paid handsomely for the villa. Part of the sale was paid for with a yacht called *Santa Barbara*. That summer, Signor Cossu sailed his newly acquired toy lazily from the Adriatic Sea to Sardinia. He moored it at Porto Cervo, the most fashionable, exclusive resort on the island, where he entertained and mingled with the rich and powerful all summer. At the end of the season, after racking up substantial mooring and maintenance costs, he became fed up with the financial commitments of maintaining such a huge asset and swiftly disposed of it by selling it to a broker.

Chapter forty two

The Slow Pace

With Floris now permanently living in Sardinia, I had sole responsibility for the daily operations of his companies. Nick's sudden dismissal meant that I now had direct control of the Praslin project, which required me to be on site more often. At times, I would commute daily by air to Praslin. Depending on my other commitments, I would sometimes stay there the whole working week, travelling home on the weekends.

If Helena was free on any given weekend, she would come and join me instead, sometimes bringing friends along. The company had temporary rented a beautiful villa on the hilltop at the resort, which had spectacular views over the Cote d'Or beach, Chauve Souris and St Pierre islets. Praslin, being underdeveloped, still enjoyed a real Creole pace of life, giving its guests a sense of wild freedom. In an idyllic location, with numerous other exotic and beautiful islands and islets close by, Praslin was quickly becoming everyone's dream holiday destination; it was especially popular with the Italian market. Many Praslinoise even learned Italian by proxy due to the sheer volume of Italian guests.

Hotel accommodation on the island was much in demand and the construction of our resort was of great importance, as no other development was planned in the near future. The shareholders were concerned about the slow pace of the construction, and were putting pressure on us to speed up the work.

We definitely had a problem with the construction. Procurement of basic building materials such as cement and timber involved shipping them in by schooner from Mahé and then transporting them from the jetty to the site using a local sub-contractor, a 'political protégé', instead of our own lorry, which led to constant obstruction and friction. He restricted site operations, invariably slowing us down. We had to negotiate and compromise to proceed and avoid any hostility; such behaviour was incomprehensible to the Praslinoise, who were normally so benevolent. We tried our best to be resourceful by producing macadam on site, blasting granite rocks that women would pound into small pieces by hand. Sand was sourced from a quarry close by and we produced our own cement blocks on the concrete base of the tennis court that that already been built.

However, our major issue was motivating the workforce to increase their workload. Overall, the Praslinoise appeared to be content with living a simpler life than their counterparts in Mahé. The lack of basic infrastructure and development on the island did not help with social progress or the welfare of the islanders. Praslin had a population of about 6,000 people with two major villages on opposite sides of the island – less than ten percent of the Seychelles population, making them a non-priority for the government. Their attitude to work was to do only what was necessary to maintain their unpretentious life. As I strolled about the construction site, I observed how many bricks the mason laid in an average day's work and came up with a plan. I discussed the urgency of our situation with the foreman, Louis, and showed him my proposal, first seeking his approval. I set the workers a target, a piece rate. The number of bricks laid would be the equivalent of a full day's pay, and twice the number of bricks laid would equal double. I knew they could do it. The workers agreed to the proposed target and suddenly I noticed that most of them achieved it by mid-morning, only to leave the site early. They could not be persuaded to stay for a double shift. We realised that the younger masons were eager to work but followed their seniors' lead. We did not want to create any friction between them and decided to wait and see if there would be any improvement. Finally, after a few weeks, they started to respond positively to the scheme and construction finally began to progress at a faster speed; I had managed to win them over!

Chapter forty three

Professor Palmieri

Italian doctors would sometimes drop by Signor Cossu's consular office to volunteer their services at the local hospital. Occasionally, some would enquire about starting a practice in the country.

One of these professionals was Professor Luciano Palmieri, a director of the oculist department at La Spezia's hospital. He was well-known and highly respected as one of the top ophthalmologists in Europe. At the time, his team were pioneering new surgical techniques that were being adopted globally.

The Seychelles Ministry of Health gladly accepted the offer of his free services, and a schedule was initiated from his arrival until his departure. His two-week holiday became fully integrated with hospital appointments, surgeries and post-operation check-ups, in between fishing trips and days at the beach. He soon began visiting the islands as often as he could, and the Victoria hospital lined up appointments for him with patients many months in advance, even though post-independence British doctors and administrators still managed the Victoria hospital with excellently trained and efficient local nurses. Professor Palmieri would eventually purchase an apartment at the Ocean Gate House and become a regular visitor to my office, establishing a good friendship between us.

On his second visit, he gave me the expert diagnosis that I had a squint and was slightly cross-eyed when I looked sideways. Having had this since birth, not many people had noticed or else they had politely never mentioned it to me. However, Professor Palmieri spotted it straight away and informed me in a matter of fact but very gentle manner.

Italians call it *strabismo di Venere,* Venus' strabismus, suggesting a certain beauty and enigma that originated from the non-aligned eyes of Botticelli's *Birth of Venus*. He suggested that he could easily fix it with an operation, but just the mention of the word operation made me abruptly change the subject.

Every time Professor Palmieri visited me, our jovial conversations would eventually turn to the subject of my eye. I had never experienced surgery before and the only time I had visited a hospital was in Sardinia to visit one of my parents. He knew I was nervous, and he tried hard to gain my trust. He was so confident that he could fix my eye with just a 'quick snip', he even went so far to say it would enhance my looks, confidence and even improve my posture! This became the litany of our meetings and eventually, feeling worn down, I responded saying, 'maybe next trip.'

The next time I saw Palmieri, he had just arrived from the airport with his bags in hand. When he entered my office, he greeted me and in the same breath reminded me eagerly of our last conversation about the surgery.

He was so persistent that I had no choice but to surrender and succumb to his will. It made his day; he was pleased and cheerful about my decision. I was not thrilled, only petrified. I had never been bothered by the imperfection that hardly anyone noticed (even Helena had never noticed it); but now it had been brought to the forefront of my attention.

Professor Palmieri planned my surgery for the following day at Victoria Hospital. He intended to open the outer layer of my eyeball to reach the muscle and make a partial cut across. This 'snip' would weaken it and re-align one eye with the other. He described in detail what he was going to do. I did not want to know and forced myself to zone out of the conversation.

Helena dropped by the hospital early the next morning. I had not slept all night because I was so nervous. I was given one of the hospital's private rooms; Palmieri had promised that I was top of the list to go in for surgery that morning.

I sat on the bed in a hospital gown waiting for my turn to go into theatre. I waited and waited as calmly as I could but as time went by my nerves got the best of me. Eventually, I had enough of waiting and was changing into my clothes when a nurse and a doctor walked in, looking at me with curiosity, and asked me what I was doing. 'I am going home,' I said, 'maybe next time, but I cannot wait any longer.'

The nurse immediately began to expertly distract me by introducing me to her colleague, an anaesthetist who had prepared a pre-operation injection to calm my nerves. I sat again on the bed and submitted to his injection. Sure enough, within minutes I fell into a dreamy, relaxed state. As I lay on the stretcher ready to go to the operating theatre, Professor Palmieri entered the room, already in scrubs, cheery and apologising profusely about the delay. His operation schedule was running late as he had had problems with his malfunctioning instruments all morning! He grinned with an excited glint in his eye, looking slightly like a mad scientist, happy to finally have his guinea pig. Too late, I laughed to myself. I was drowsy from the injection and powerless to turn back now.

I woke up in my room with a smiling nurse looking down at me. The operation had gone well and there had been no problems with the instruments during my surgery! Professor Palmieri visited me soon after and told me that it had been a remarkably successful operation. I had to stay the night at the hospital for observation and I would be discharged the following morning after a quick check up.

Chapter forty four

Refusal to Exit

As time passed after the split of the group, I saw Signor Cossu less and less; our personal relationship had ground to a halt as he continued disposing of his investments. He had sold his travel company, Blue Safari, to an Italian associate and the Pirates Arms complex was also the subject of the final stage of negotiations.

One day, he summoned me to a meeting at his offices, asking that I write to the bank to relieve him of his personal guarantees for the SOGIS Ocean Gate House debts. As he tried to convince me that there had been some sort of misunderstanding with the bank arrangements, I quickly saw through his tricks, his age-old routine of attempting to manipulate me like one of his subordinates. However, he was not my boss anymore and when I disagreed, a bitter argument ensued. He was not happy with my sharp reply, and I respectfully left his office, feeling a bit guilty.

Unexpectedly, I bumped into him on the beach at Beau Vallon a few weeks later. It was as if our last encounter had never happened. He asked me if I would be interested in being appointed Consul, as his replacement. I asked if he was leaving since I had heard rumours he was. He remained vague. I did not take him seriously, as now I knew him better. Being wary, I rebuffed his offer. Signora Cossu had left the country in earnest. Signor Cossu shut down his office and dismissed Nicole, the secretary, and was surely preparing to follow her.

A few weeks later, without revealing his planned departure to a soul, Cossu turned up at the airport, only to be stopped by the immigration authorities and refused permission to leave the country. He was asked to visit the Revenue Tax office to regularize his outstanding tax debts.

The following day he went to the tax office, and somehow convinced them to issue a permit allowing him out of the country, as his departure was only temporary, for a 'short holiday', he said. A few days later he left Seychelles for good, incognito. No marching band, no glitz, no one to bid him farewell. Sadly, Corrado Cossu's reign in the Seychelles had ended. I had witnessed both the dramatic rise and fall of his empire!

Chapter forty five

Threats and Intimidation

The uncertainty of the Seychelles government's policies made foreign investors and local businesspeople wary. Capital funds were withdrawn and sent abroad; foreign currency exchange dried up. In an attempt to resolve the situation, the authorities were forced to impose foreign exchange controls. The government took control of all import and export trading through parastatal companies. The country's socialist model structure slowly began to take root. René's policies continued to alienate the upper and middle classes and foreign investors. The labour workforce, with the help of the union, resented the new socialist rhetoric and the way the government fomented hostility towards the expat community, painting foreigners as oppressors.

Some party supporters took advantage by claiming a close relationship with the head of state. They acted like they were the new masters, untouchable by the authorities, expecting no retaliation. They exploited the situation by generating fear among the general public. They instigated a kind of pay-back situation and even engaged in racketeering, asserting themselves with threats and intimidation.

As I mentioned, at our import-export business, the Builder Centre, we were forced to make use of a local truck company instead of our own to transport goods from the docks to the warehouse and to accept their extortionate tariff. This was extended to our operation on Praslin. The intimidations and personal threats became profoundly disturbing. When goods were stolen or went missing from the premises, we were defenceless. When we reported thefts to the authorities, no action was taken. We even took it upon ourselves to write a letter to the president to make him aware of the deplorable situation we were in.

On one occasion, the discovery of a great quantity of timber that had gone missing from our site brought me to the office of Dr Ferrari, Minister of Planning and Development. His response was to warn me that, should I sack the foreman, who happened to be his associate, I would be made persona non grata and removed from the country within 24 hours. We were, at the time, utterly powerless and had no alternative other than to accept this blackmail.

Assoonastheprojectterminated,monthslater,Isackedtheforeman. I could not accept this ransom situation. I have yet to hear from Dr Ferrari.

Chapter forty six

The Far East Expedition, November 1980

The Praslin project complex was originally intended to be a self-contained residence. But due to the high demand for hotel accommodation on the island, the shareholders decided to turn the nearly completed complex into a hotel resort and integrate the new hotel's features into the original design. However, Mr Floris was adamant that few modifications should be implemented as the changes would cause a substantial rise in construction costs. I raised the opinion that this would be detrimental to the hotel's functionality, leaving it a disjointed, hybrid and unorthodox experience. Mr Floris agreed with me but for contractual reasons did not want to expand the new concept. Future management and guests would have to accept and live with such dysfunctions in return for a holiday in paradise!

We were finally approaching completion, and we just needed to procure furnishings for the hotel. This was the best news we had had for a long time, and everyone's mood lifted. We decided to embark on an expedition to visit the Far East factories in search of suppliers, and I planned our travel itinerary. Mr Floris returned with his wife to join me on the trip; neither of us had been to that part of the world before. Armed with a list of manufacturers and distributers, we set off.

We boarded a British Airways flight to Colombo on its weekly run to London via the 'Alaska route' that connected South Africa to London via Anchorage, Tokyo, Hong Kong, Colombo, and the Seychelles, ending in Johannesburg before returning on the same route. The next day we flew from Colombo to Singapore on Swissair, and then took a Philippines Airlines flight to Manila. Then it was on to Taipei with China Airlines, Cathay Pacific to Hong Kong, Thai International into Bangkok,

Thai International *back* to Colombo and finally British Airways back to Mahé. A few days later, the Floris's returned to Sardinia.

Overall, we visited nine countries in fourteen days, including Malaysia and China. We generated an enormous number of contacts and visited many factories and suppliers. We stayed in beautiful hotels and were treated throughout with a professionalism and a courtesy that we had never encountered before.

The Far East executives had a cordial, friendly approach to doing business. Their politeness extended from the moment they welcomed us at the airport or hotel, escorting us throughout our stay to visit factories. They all seemed distinctly delighted to make our acquaintance.

Mr Floris always exercised due diligence when it came to money. He had given me a precise and detailed budget for the entire journey. However, I devised a plan to soften him up to allow us a pleasurable experience; this was not just a working trip after all, it was also a once in a lifetime opportunity!

Floris had a reputation for being careful with spending, but I recognised it as stinginess. This became apparent while at restaurants, where it was social etiquette to always follow the boss' choice. When Mr Floris ordered, he would always choose the cheapest possible dish on the menu.

My first opportunity to implement my plan came in Singapore, when at dinner he asked me to order two steak and chips for him and his wife. Upon studying the menu, I ordered a grilled lobster for myself, in defiance of the regular protocol. When the waiter served us, Floris could not believe his eyes: they were served meagre-looking steaks and I was served a whole, sizzling giant grilled lobster, cascading off my plate. He and his wife looked at each other puzzled, with outraged expressions. How dare I order a lobster!

I knew exactly what there were thinking – to offer reassurance, I showed them the menu and explained that in the Far East, seafood was less expensive than beef. 'Well, now we know,' Floris said, 'from now on seafood every dinner.' He clearly yearned for my lobster, drooling throughout dinner.

In Manila, my budget only allowed me to book a four-star hotel, but our Filipino contact could not understand why we were not staying at the five-star Manila Hotel for an extra $20 a night. So as to not look tight-fisted to the supplier, Floris consented to a transfer to the luxury hotel. We all genuinely enjoyed the lavish treatment at this fabulous hotel. At dinner, with seafood, Mr Floris even allowed us to order a bottle of white wine!

It was infectious; I had corrupted his spending and convinced him to enjoy the moment. His wife was incredulous about what I had managed to do, but we both knew that, sadly, his spree would not last.

My relationship with Mr Floris developed from that trip and there was a strengthened feeling of trust and honesty; we both admired and respected each other. He relied on me and was completely dependent on me for his Seychelles investments, and I was happy to deliver my best and not to disappoint him.

Chapter forty seven

Short of Cash

Despite being very profitable on the books, SOGIS was somehow always short of cash and in need of financial support to complete projects. The interlinking of shareholders, crossing over between the developer and the construction company, had become a hindrance as SOGIS only partially received what it invoiced for the work. Neither of main shareholders, Cossu and Floris, had ever paid anything towards their respective shares.

The sale of Ocean Gate House should have replenished the SOGIS bank accounts, but instead the money was sent abroad, leaving the company to deal with huge bank loans. When the Cossu Group was split up, the bank loan was divided in two, with each to be personally responsible for repayment for their share. With half of the loan relieved, SOGIS still had to repay Mr Floris's portion.

I had to manage on my own without Mr Floris's financial support and guidance. Although I was in charge and in control of the situation, I had no means to satisfy the bankers. The task of negotiating a new loan was frustrated by the restrictions of previous arrangements, and our bankers at Barclays were not prepared to finance our new ongoing project at Praslin without any guarantees. After all, to them, I was merely an employee! They wanted repayments for the already existing debts and verbal, or written promises no longer satisfied them; tangible assets were needed for reassurance.

Each month, I struggled to make ends meet during the construction of the Praslin Resort. I opened an account with the Chartered Standard Bank and managed to obtain a few short bridging loans to oversee payments due on a month-to-month basis. SOGIS was surviving hand to mouth.

One particular month, the payroll went unpaid for two days, leading to the beginnings of a riot. While trying to calm the situation, I was threatened with a trowel to my neck by one of the workers on site. For the first time, I felt let down by Mr Floris.

Mr Carta, a minority shareholder of SOGIS and Builder Centre, was in the country on holiday at the time; I had not seen much of him before but he was always jovial and smiled easily. He had informal manner in business matters and was generally more approachable and friendly to the staff. He ran a successful, thriving business in Sardinia. He was not a particularly good flyer, requiring tablets to calm his nerves, but he loved boats and fishing. He spoke no English and his elementary French was fragmented; he was only ever able to put key words together to communicate.

He had once dreamed of moving to the islands with his young family, seeking the good life in the Seychelles. His investment was driven primarily by his friendship with Cossu and Floris. But the unforeseen events shaping the political climate kept him away and his original desires slowly faded.

He was sympathetic to my frustrations and understood the difficulties of dealing with the dire, day-to-day financial situation, on top of all the other issues SOGIS now faced. I took advantage of his presence and dragged him to the bank to sign personal guarantees for the bridging loan. Mr Carta still reminds me today of when we had to share a toast at the Pirates Arms that day, as we were skint.

Chapter forty eight

Mercenaries

On 25 November 1981, just after five in the afternoon, I left my office at Ocean Gate House and, as usual, drove home to St Louis in my yellow Moke. The doors and louvred windows were shut; no one was home. Laika stood patiently by the veranda to welcome me, wagging his tail in his ever-playful mood; he was happy to see me and was longing for a scratch behind the ear. I entered the living room and opened two windows to let in the light. I approached the bar and switched on the radio, deciding to go to Beau Vallon for my after-work swim. In the bedroom, I grabbed a pair of swim trunks, shed my office clothes and pulled my trunks on.

Radio Seychelles was playing Dr Hook's *A Little Bit More* when it was suddenly interrupted by a male broadcaster reporting an unusual message. I was not bothered at first, but as I moved back to the living room, I started to pay full attention to the message that was being repeated in English and Creole: 'Attention, attention! All military personnel to report to base.'

Feeling a bit unsure, I hesitated. What was the purpose of this emergency call-out of military personnel on the radio? This had never happened before. Something was wrong. The message was transmitted continuously, without interruptions. With only my swim trunks on, I popped out to the veranda and stared across the main road. Everything looked ordinary, a few cars passed by, and people were walking around as normal. Back in the living room, the radio kept broadcasting the same message.

I picked up the phone and dialled the number for Vacoa Village. Helena answered, as she was still at work. Firmly, I told her to come back home at once, without giving her an explanation. As I put the handset down, a cold male voice came onto the air, ordering everyone to return home immediately and remain inside until further notice. The authorities had imposed a curfew, no one should be outside, and anyone found on the street would be shot on sight.

This was, indeed, a deeply serious situation. I nervously waited for Helena to return home. Within 20 minutes of my telephone call, she turned up. She drove straight up to the house and parked her car next to mine under our red flame tree. She asked if I was unwell, as she could not understand the urgency in my voice on the phone. As I started to explain the situation, gunshots could be heard in the distance.

We could not identify the location of what now sounded like a serious skirmish. We were very frightened and watched as people on the street quickly rushed into their houses. The road became deserted with fewer cars passing by, until they stopped completely. We moved inside and wondered what was happening. Helena wanted to return to Vacoa Village to be with her guests and offer them reassurance. I advised against it, as the radio message was still broadcasting, repeatedly warning everyone to stay indoors.

Sunset was fast approaching, and, in the dark, we could see the flares of the explosions coming from the direction of the airport, emitting red and orange hues, tainting the colours of the beautiful sunset. The gunfire was intermittently intense, with the bangs getting heavier and louder, breaking the calm of our otherwise peaceful surroundings. The sky filled with clouds of dark smoke; a battle had clearly erupted. Only the large fruit bats, the flying foxes, *sousouri*, were undeterred by the commotion – with their large wingspan they kept coming to roost on the tall mango trees at the back of the property.

We later learnt that earlier that afternoon, a scheduled Royal Swazi Airways flight, a twinjet Fokker F28, had landed at Seychelles

International Airport from Manzini in Swaziland. On board, disguised as tourists and members of a rugby team, was a group of 53 mercenary soldiers, carrying their own weapons, with the aim of bringing down René's government in a coup that would re-install the former president, James Mancham.

Their operation was unexpectedly triggered when an alert customs official spotted an AK-47 assault rifle at the bottom of one of the mercenary's bags. The airport was taken over, with the mercenary soldiers stationed strategically around the entrance and arrivals area.

A gun-battle ensued with local soldiers based at a nearby army camp. On high alert, the Seychelles authorities had the airport surrounded by soldiers. The only way for the mercenaries to escape was to regain control of the F28 Royal Swazi aircraft and fly back to South Africa. The Seychelles forces, led by their Tanzanian commander, launched a heavy mortar attack on the airport aiming to destroy the F28 twinjet. A mortar fell on the aircraft, rendering it useless.

The legendary Colonel Michael Hoare, an Irish ex-Congo veteran, was leading the mercenaries. Hoare was trapped, with the battle lost and no escape in sight, but he had a moment of relief when his man at the control tower picked up a transmission from an incoming aircraft. With the battle raging, a spot of luck had finally come his way.

The weekly commercial Air India Boeing 707 aircraft approached for landing. Flight AI224 was flying from Sainsbury to Bombay with a stopover in the Seychelles. Captain Umesh Saxena, commander of the Air India flight, had no idea of the power struggle on the ground. He realised the trouble only once the aircraft had engaged for landing, already too late to turn around, as they were short on fuel.

After landing on the runway, the aircraft came to a stop and taxied to the terminal. The mercenaries surrounded the aircraft and Hoare boarded the plane with a few of his men. The passengers aboard were made to remain quietly seated while Hoare negotiated a way out with the captain, hijacking the aircraft with the passengers and the remaining forty-five mercenaries on board.

The Boeing 707 was quickly refuelled and, in the dark of night, using the runway from north to south so they would head directly out over the open ocean rather than risk being shot down, it took off. Captain Saxena was only given notification of the destination once airborne. One mercenary was killed on the battlefield and seven others had to cover the escape by holding some Seychellois hostages at the terminal. After take-off, the mortars continued to fall onto the airport, as the army was not aware of the situation for quite some time.

In the morning, the remaining mercenaries surrendered and were arrested, while the hostages were released, unharmed. The Air India flight landed safely at the Durban military airport, where the mercenaries were arrested for hijacking, and the passengers freed.

Unaware of the ongoing tumultuous situation, Helena visited her mum to reassure her that we were available if she needed help. She barricaded herself inside as Helena left. We closed our shutters and doors and barely touched our dinner. Helena was concerned for her guests' wellbeing, as she had not had the chance to see or talk to them and knew they must have been panicking just as we were. The radio broadcast ended at 8 p.m., like always, and the transmission went off the air. I left the radio switched on in case of any further news. The telephone remained silent. All the commotion left Laika agitated; his barking became urgent and constant as he ran up and down in the garden. The unfamiliar noises certainly made him anxious. We decided to allow him to sleep inside the house in the living room to calm his nerves. He hid under the table and, after a while, settled down for the night. We went to bed soon after and tried to get some rest, but sleep would not come.

When the gunshots and mortar fire ceased before daybreak, silence and tranquillity returned. It was not until 7 a.m. that the radio came alive with President René airing a message that the Seychelles had been attacked by mercenaries trying to overthrow his government, but that the enemies had been repelled, rounded up and arrested. He said they were in full control of the situation. For security measures, he imposed a 24-hour curfew; no one was allowed out until further notice. We had to remain home and isolated for the time being. We had woken up to a sunrise of uncertainty.

Roadblocks were set up and the militia was mobilised on the roads. The known sympathizers of the old government were brutally rounded up and incarcerated. What followed was a full crackdown, with yet more restrictions on individual liberties and freedom. We did not know how much worse things could get and I began to wonder what would happen to us expatriates. We spent all day by the radio, waiting for further news. I made a few local telephone calls to fellow Italian compatriots and friends, trying to gather information on evacuation plans for foreigners to leave the country. Cossu had been our consular representation and, now that he was gone, along with his post, we wondered who could help if the situation became dangerous and we needed repatriation. The French, American and British all had diplomatic representation on the island, and some of my compatriots had the firm belief that those embassies would help us.

Everyone was frightened. In the midst of these moments of pure terror, *radio bambou* was in full swing with conspiracy claims – rumours were spread that a Russian submarine had been spotted in the distance at Beau Vallon ready for an invasion! It was known that the Russians had military and political interests in the country, but the story sounded hard to believe, even though anything seemed plausible in that moment.

As dusk came, we settled down into a more peaceful atmosphere, in contrast to the chaos of the night before. Helena managed to speak to the guests individually by phone, calling the reception telephone at the Village. She reassured them that, despite the volatile situation, she would remain in contact and report further news as soon as possible.

The next morning Helena spoke to an officer in charge at the main police station in Victoria and was granted a travel permit to visit her guests at Vacoa Village. I decided to accompany her; it was an opportunity to leave the house and ascertain what the situation was. On the way there, the roads were empty of cars. I saw only a few people who had dared to break the curfew, desperately seeking essential food supplies, gathered around the Indian grocery shops.

When we arrived at the Beau Vallon police station, we were stopped at a roadblock of armed soldiers. The local militia had not been trained in army regulations and their weapons looked brand new; I doubted if they knew how to use them. We were confronted and questioned at gunpoint while Helena presented our travel permit and calmly explained why we were breaking curfew. As they looked over our papers, I felt frightened but tried to remain calm. Since the roadblocks had been so suddenly assembled, the chain of command between police, army and militia was at odds with each other. After a few agonising minutes of the soldiers, with their newfound authority, scrutinising our car and papers, they let us pass and we finally reached the resort.

Guests had gathered around the reception. They we were all fearful and anxious, with hundreds of questions, of which Helena could only answer very few. She could only provide words of comfort. We stayed the couple of hours we had been permitted by the militia and then returned home to St Louis. As we reached the same roadblock at the Beau Vallon police station, we luckily encountered the same militia patrol that had questioned us on the way in. Recognizing the car, they sped us through without any more hindrance.

The next morning, the government announced a dusk-to-dawn curfew. We were allowed outside in daylight, from 7 a.m. to 7 p.m. Things calmed down a little as all the conspiracy claims turned out to be merely *kankan*. The government seemed to be in control of the situation, and the army and militia were out in force to protect various government buildings along with that of Radio Seychelles. I drove to our office in town and managed to speak with our site managers over the phone. We were able to draw up a plan of action and, with precautionary measures set in place, we decided to continue our day-to-day operations. The imposed curfew did not affect our work routine. In the office, Labonté kept me informed of the latest political developments from *radio bambou* with the help of his wife, Itala, who also worked as secretary to an influential Indian businessman.

Chapter forty nine

Isolated

The airport was in critical condition and all operations had halted. Taking the brunt of the battle, the runway and terminal had been hard-hit by mortars, rendering both unusable for commercial aircraft. The Seychelles was isolated from the rest of the world once more. Holidaying tourists were very frightened of the political situation they found themselves in and desperately wanted to leave. When they heard of the airport's closure and the cancellation of all scheduled flights, they became restless and anxious. The government prioritised getting the airport functional again and contractors were sent to clear the damage. A few days after the attempted coup, the runway tarmac had been sufficiently patched.

After a week of uncertainty, the authorities finally gave clearance for Kenya Airways to operate its route from Nairobi. This was followed up by a weekly Aeroflot flight to Moscow via Aden. But the European airlines stayed away, as the insurance to operate in a country with political unrest was deemed too costly. As the Seychelles' economy relied heavily on tourism for its foreign currency exchange, the loss of this revenue was a massive blow for the country. Ministers were dispatched to Europe to seek financial help and political support.

Rumours abounded that ex-president Mancham and Gerard Hoarau were behind the attempted coup and that it had been financed by foreign investors like Mario Ricci. The operation had also apparently been orchestrated with the awareness and help of the South African government. Ricci had discreetly kept up his relationship with the exiled Hoarau even while actively courting René. It appeared he had played the Machiavellian role brilliantly, with deception and deviousness, ready to change sides at a moment's notice, if events necessitated it.

Meanwhile, the population fell deeper into misery, frustration and grief. For President René to hang onto power, he needed not only faithful cabinet ministers and soldiers but also loyal citizens. He sought to identify the 'enemies' of the regime and accused them of conspiracy against the government in order to have them imprisoned or preferably made scarce by way of exile from the country.

For the last four and a half years, René had slowly but steadily tightened the screw. Any individual who publicly resisted his regime was vulnerable to threats, intimidation, kidnapping or worse. Government posts had already been given to his supporters and revolutionary activists, with the non-political Seychellois and white civil servant staff replaced. This faux authority was distributed among the new administration officials; they were the elite now. Corruption flourished among the new officials now that they were the masters. The network of government informers and spies became widespread, creating a climate of terror across the country. Revolution was costly to maintain in paradise.

Collectively, the Seychellois were suffering in silence. Creole society is a multi-racial mix of white, black and Asian, with black people making up the majority. With a small population of just 70,000, the exile and absence of the well-off Seychellois had a substantial economic impact on the people. Speaking out against the regime was dangerous and one had to know whom one's friends and enemies were.

After a few weeks of strict curfew, the government eventually relaxed restrictions and extended curfew to midnight, but our lives were still affected by the political events. Helena and I carried on with our social life as best as we could, as all Seychellois tried to do. On a few occasions we broke the curfew, returning from the Beoliere Club past midnight and had to endure the militia roadblocks when crossing Victoria. We became complacent about the process of showing our ID's and gave our usual answers to the usual questions, unafraid. We became less bothered, passing through the checkpoints unafraid, although a bit intoxicated at times. We noticed that when Helena mentioned she was Guy Morel's sister, they always let us through easily and without hassle.

Chapter fifty

A Fishing Expedition

Gradually, I saw more and more of Nello. Because of the decline in tourists visiting the islands, his business had been affected and his trading volume had dropped drastically. In the end, he was forced to give up his lovely shop on Victoria's main boulevard, making his staff redundant. He moved share premises with a local silversmith jeweller at the Victoria mall but slowly his business deteriorated. Now, with more time for himself, he would turn up unannounced and with increasing frequency at my office, sometimes more than I would have liked him to.

Mr Carta returned to pay a short visit and see what was going on in paradise, arriving without his delightful wife. He was trying to make sense of his investments and their future here, if they had any at all. He had had lengthy conversations with Floris back in Sardinia, most likely in an attempt to strategize a way forward. He wanted to take a short visit to the site at Praslin and suggested a fishing expedition while there.

I hated boats and fishing all together. I was hardly a keen sailor – on the contrary, I was lousy and seasick-prone, so I avoided boat trips at all costs. Back when I had fulfilled my National Service in mainland Italy, I had suffered an eight-hour ferry ride from Olbia to Civitavecchia and had been seasick throughout the journey. Just the thought of *il mal di mare* was a nightmare for me. I would rather fly if at all possible. I had learned that to avoid motion sickness, the boat had to have powerful enough engines to speed its way through the waves; it was the ups and downs of the swells that made me nauseous and sick.

Mr Carta, however, managed to persuade me to go deep-sea fishing with him and I asked Nello to join us on the trip. It was March, the rainy season had just ended, and it was perfect weather for fishing. I booked a half-day deep-sea trip leaving the following morning, specifically requesting a fast vessel. As daylight broke, we made our way to the meeting point at the Cote d'Or beach. We were scheduled to return at noon.

The day before, Nello had talked non-stop about his fishing trip experiences at Tanga, off the Tanzanian coast. I had never heard these stories before, only his bush tales from the deep jungle. I had never imagined him to be a good sailor, but he sounded like the ultimate seadog!

We boarded the tender with a boy who rowed us to our fishing boat, which was anchored in deeper water. The vessel was an impressive 37-foot central console, a light blue Bertram. As we got closer, however, we realised that it had definitely seen better days. We were assured that it was fast, as it was powered by two large Volvo Penta engines.

We were assisted on board and introduced to the crew, consisting of the skipper and two young helpers. We were welcomed and, wasting no time, we swiftly departed. Soon enough, the two powerful engines were in full throttle. As we gained speed, the keel pulled out of the water and forcefully cut through the calm ocean, leaving a powerful wake behind us.

I had purposely skipped breakfast, as I wanted to enjoy the trip as much as possible, with no surprises. Subconsciously, I had horrible anxiety about becoming seasick. I tried to populate my mind with good thoughts, which left me feeling optimistic. The sky was bright and blue with the usual light grey clouds floating by. Everything was fantastic; I finally felt able to relax, far away from the problems plaguing us at the office.

We headed northeast, and were scheduled to reach the 'drop off' in around an hour. Our destination was the edge of the Seychelles bank plateau, some 28 miles from Praslin. The edge drops off sharply, it is a couple of thousand meters to the ocean floor, and the area was known as a fantastic spot for big game fishing. The boys prepared some fishing line, and we caught a couple of bonito on the way there. As soon as Mr Carta caught one, Nello reeled in another. The boat slowed to bring in the catch, and soon enough we were on our way again. It was a good start, a good omen. Mr Carta was the real fisherman among us. We looked forward to reaching our destination so that the real fishing could start in earnest, and we could be relaxing and chitchatting under the early morning sun on the platform by the stern.

The boat slowed down once again. We must have another catch, I thought, something big. I did not see any activity from the boys; the fishing rods were standing still in their holders, with their lines showing no tension, no fish were hooked. But the boat continued losing speed and suddenly the two powerful engines shut down altogether. Puzzled, the skipper unsuccessfully tried to restart the engines. A slight hitch, I imagined. I asked the skipper why the engines had stopped. He replied that was all was good. He said not to worry: 'We will be up and running in a few moments.'

But I *was* worried. With all power lost, we were now keeping rhythm with the rise and fall of the waves. I excused myself from Mr Carta and Nello and walked towards the bow, gazing at the sky, and I turned my head out to see, seeking a fresh breeze. I stood waiting patiently, silently praying for our boat to quickly regain power.

More time passed and I decided to sit outside the front of the cabin. I lay back and stared straight towards the horizon. I dreaded being unwell; I needed to distract myself and trick my mind out of making me sick. The wind began to gather strength and the sea became choppy. The skipper was working on the engines with the help of the boys, who passed tools over to him, one-by-one, on demand. While I had been preoccupied with focusing on my own wellbeing, I now realised that Nello felt unwell, too. He had left Mr Carta on the stern and found refuge inside the cabin, where he was lying down on a couch.

Mr Carta found himself alone so he busied himself trying to find out what was happening. He spoke in Italian, which neither crewmember understood, so they decided it was best to ignore him. This irritated him greatly, so he promptly stalked over to me and began loudly voicing his concerns. Calmly, I tried to tell him that the skipper had everything under control, and there was no reason to worry. As I kept my eyes focused on the horizon, I feebly reassured him that, soon enough, we would be on our way.

He demanded that I do something. 'I know nothing about boats and engines,' I breathed weakly. 'We have to remain calm and trust in the skipper. Do not put extra pressure on him.'

The skipper was frantically trying to fix the broken-down engines. After some time spent tinkering, he reasoned that the cooling systems had failed, causing the engines to overheat and shut down. He attempted to restart the engines a few times, unsuccessfully.

We found ourselves adrift in the middle of the ocean, surrounded by nothing but open water for miles. I decided not to move from my safe spot. Nello was down below, terribly seasick, and could not be coaxed outside by the skipper to get some fresh air.

Mr Carta paced from the stern to the bow, gesticulating and muttering to himself as no one else was listening. More than an hour had passed and the engines remained silent. Mr Carta started to become concerned and lost his patience. He demanded that the skipper radio our position to the Port Master in Victoria. I translated this into English and shouted the request to the skipper from my perch.

'*Inn kase*' – 'it is broken', he replied. We were shocked to learn that the boat's VHF radio was either out of range or not working at all. Mr Carta lost his cool; this news infuriated him. His English was non-existent, and his French was sporadic; nonetheless, he shouted at the skipper, '*Je suis le captain en Italie! J'ai un grand bateaux.*' He had managed to string together a sentence with enough French words to express his frustration and anger. It was followed with, '*Incoscienti,*' or 'You reckless lot'.

A feeling of dread and fear settled over Mr Carta. He quickly assessed the situation: no power, no radio, no food provisions and very little water, surrounded only by the open ocean. Nello was throwing up down below in the cabin, too incapacitated to move. I had managed so far to keep my *mal di mare* at bay, but Nello and I were both too preoccupied to realise the severity of our predicament.

The blistering midday sun was beating relentlessly down on us. I sensed the heat burning my skin, but I felt too paralyzed to move to the shade, feeling only the need to concentrate on the horizon. I was in control, but the fear of vomiting held me there.

The skipper was busy dismantling parts of the engine. He was clearly an experienced man and his demeanour was entirely calm – I wondered if this has happened before. The focused energy with which he worked on the problem reassured me. The boys seemed to have a similar attitude as they were messing around together. However, the confidence of the crew was of no comfort to Mr Carta. He had lost any trust in the skipper, deeming him to be unprofessional. The defective cooling system and malfunctioning VHF radio was unacceptable, and the authorities should confiscate his tourist fishing licence, he said.

But all this big talk was for later, now we needed to be rescued from this perilous situation. Mr Carta felt helpless, constrained by his thoughts and with no one to listen to him, which continued to infuriate him. He resumed striding up and down the length of the boat, venting his anger and concerns to himself. He feared the worst, being adrift for days, not being found, and perhaps ending up on the Tanzanian coastline miles and miles away. I was no longer in the mood to humour him. I remained confident that our crew would save the day.

The boat floated aimlessly for hours. All we hoped to see now was land. Suddenly, breaking the monotonous sound of the waves hitting the hull, the engines woke, both kickstarting with a reassuring roar and a burst of grey fumes that dispersed in the air as quickly as it had appeared. As soon as the engines started, they stopped again; the skipper had decided to use one engine at a time as a precaution. Mr Carta cheered; it sounded promising.

Our fishing trip ended before it had even started. We headed back home on one engine, trying to make our way back to Praslin. A long way out, we all pondered quietly to ourselves if we were going to make it. Our crippled vessel would not permit us to return with any speed. We had to travel slowly to make sure the engine would not overheat again and shut down. Mr Carta sat next to the skipper, making sure that he kept a constant and reasonable speed. He seemed the most scared of us all, but as we were now moving and no longer adrift, he regained some of his composure. We kept hearing him say 'piano, piano.' He was showing definite signs of relief, but we were still a long way out. We were expected to return by noon, but we were long past that, still on the high seas.

Meanwhile, Helena, who had been with me earlier in Praslin, arrived on the beach at Cote d'Or only to find no sign of the boat. She waited. The boat owner soon turned up and could not understand why the boat was late, either.

Our progress was incredibly slow. Once we sighted land on the horizon at last, we all cheered loudly and breathed a sigh of relief, including the crew! Maybe the skipper had hidden his concerns after all, as he finally relaxed and gave us a genuine smile. We were finally close enough that we could even swim back to one of the islands. It was just before dusk when we finally reached Cote d'Or. A number of people had gathered as word spread of our disappearance. The police were there too. It had been an agonising day for Helena and the boat owner. We were physically and emotionally exhausted from the ordeal; I was burned beet red by the sun, but thankfully not sick! Mr Carta kept moaning about the experience. Nello had shown up on the bow just before reaching the shore, feeling like himself again. We gave our statement to the police – frankly, we were just glad to be alive and well. The owner apologised profusely for the misadventure and didn't charge us for the trip.

Mr Carta was certainly not prepared to pay for the fishing trip, but it pleased him that the owner in addition offered to charge him half price for a future trip. Apart the business situation, he ended up being pleased to return to Sardinia with a good adventure story to tell.

Chapter fifty one

Back to his Farmhouse

Signor Cossu returned to his farmhouse villa in Sardinia. After escaping his mess in the Seychelles, he and his wife enjoyed life to the fullest, continuing to spend voraciously to support their luxurious lifestyle, travelling across Europe intermingling with friends, entertaining and socializing with affluent local contacts. But Cossu soon became restless after being out of the action and longed to start a new business venture.

His *Azienda Agricola* was the most important dairy farm in the region, supplying milk to the local dairy factory. He decided to get involved in the dairy plant's operations and somehow, he quickly managed to be nominated as the president of the dairy company.

I happened to be in Sardinia on my summer holidays that June when he asked me to visit him. He wanted to see me, no doubt to talk about the Seychelles and his new business enterprise. After all, we had completely lost touch after his abrupt departure. Out of curiosity and a lingering respect, I obliged his request and visited his office at the dairy plant in Oristano.

Signor Cossu proudly showed me his grand design plans to expand activity and introduce new products, excitedly asserting that the acquisition of new equipment and machinery would create a more efficient and profitable company! The plant would be like no other, absolutely unique in Sardinia. He had hired the best engineers for the project, having already secured backing from shareholders and the board. He was serious, and once again very convincing. I was merely a spectator, but I felt like he wanted my approval!

Knowing him as I did, I doubted that he possessed the skills required to go through with such plans. He always aimed too high, biting off more than he could chew, ignoring budgeting issues. He made too many impulsive and extravagant purchases without thinking them through. His adventurous ego remained dominant, and this superseded everything and everyone.

Sure enough, halfway through the refurbishment, the company ran out of funds and, shockingly, the dairy plant went bankrupt. The resulting consequences were for everyone else to bear. The shareholders were bewildered, as they had expected greatness. Once again, 'Corradino' tried to preserve his delusions of grandeur but failed resoundingly.

Months later, his wife Lily was suddenly diagnosed with cancer and after a short illness, she passed away. Signor Cossu decided that he had had enough of cattle farming and sold the entire farm, dividing it into three lots. The dairy farm and the extensive agricultural land were sold to a local farmer, and the farmhouse villa to a retired professor from Bologna, but he kept the stable with the tennis courts, swimming pool and surrounding land to start a self-catering business with a new local partner.

Chapter fifty two

Unresolved Issues

Our newest project was planning the design of a new hotel just down the road from the Praslin Beach Resort. Finally, with planning permission granted, our Italian investors were ready to begin construction. The directors regularly visited our office to finalise operations and we were preparing to move our entire workforce onto the new site. However, due to the recent coup attempt, the company had to retreat. Doubting the viability of the project due to the present political climate, they decided to halt any investment.

The only large project on the horizon was the construction of Independence House in Victoria, financed by the government. Because of Mr Floris's commitments, we decided not to tender for the work. Following this decision, SOGIS had run out of work. I had no choice but to lay off the workforce at the workshop at Pointe Conan and the mechanics at the garage. I kept a small team on Praslin for maintenance work at the resort.

At Builders Centre, I had already changed managers twice because of the continual theft and disappearance of stock. Construction materials from South Africa and Rhodesia were deliberately re-invoiced as goods originating in Swaziland to avoid the apartheid sanctions. This administrative re-invoicing created a surcharge on goods that our South-African manager pocketed, so he was sacked.

The firm had many unresolved issues to deal with, along with new ones mounting up daily. The manager manipulated the company's books and, unless we implemented a direct control of its daily running, it was impossible to keep our grip on a business that otherwise would have been successful and profitable.

Not only that, but our warehouse, along with a large amount of stock, was also partially destroyed due to a fire. This turned out to be arson, committed either by a disgruntled contractor or a sacked staff member. We were lucky to have been able to claim damages from the insurance.

Chapter fifty three

To Freedom

The consular position remained vacant following Cossu's departure. Instead, Italian tourists turned up at my office in search of opportunities to invest in the country. It was interesting to see how people fell so easily in love with the Seychelles, just as I had. The islands were like a siren, seducing anyone who set foot on their shores. People often sought out a reason to stay, or at least to return, typically by establishing a business or investing in property.

One day, an Italian civil engineer named Mr Varnero came to visit me at the office. He owned a large construction company in Yemen and wanted to invest. I thought this was a stroke of luck, considering that Mr Floris had already floated the idea of disposing of SOGIS. His construction company was experienced and financially secure: potentially the perfect partners. I quietly contemplated whether I could persuade them to take over SOGIS in some way or another.

Varnero explained that his family had arrived in Ethiopia in the 1920s as part of Mussolini's plan to colonise the newly annexed African country with thousands of fellow citizens. His father, a newly graduated civil engineer, had established a construction company upon his arrival and begun to contribute substantially to the development of Ethiopia's infrastructure. Over the years, they had been involved in building roads, railways, dams, hydroelectric plants and many important buildings in Addis Ababa and elsewhere.

After Ethiopia's independence from Italy, many Italians remained in the country under the full pardon of Haile Selassie, who had returned from his exile in the UK. To continue with the modernisation of his country, the emperor asked the Italian construction companies to remain in Ethiopia. Varnero had decided to stay and explore the opportunities on offer, going on to build the Hilton Hotel and National Bank of Ethiopia. The emperor wanted iconic monuments such as the Africa Hall erected to demonstrate that 'it was possible to construct grand buildings here, too.'

Haile Selassie was eventually overthrown in a brutal coup d'état in 1974 that was followed by a civil war, plunging the country into total chaos. The one-party communist regime that replaced Haile Selassie imposed tough restrictions on the nation that resulted in severe hardship. Properties were confiscated, and foreigners and wealthy locals were stripped of their assets. The civil war was followed by more atrocities, repression, violence and famine, resulting in the death of millions.

In midst of the tragedy, Varnero's father suffered a heart attack but was able to be evacuated, with approximately 22,000 compatriots back to the motherland. Varnero had remained with his older brother to manage the only asset the government had left them, the construction company.

The government imposed tough foreign travel restrictions to avoid the brain drain of highly skilled workers needed for the country's continued development. Permission to travel was required from the authorities and the terms were convoluted. Families were never to travel together; a holiday trip abroad meant separation – the husband would only be allowed to travel once the wife returned and vice versa – meaning family members acted as guarantors to vouch for each other's return. It made it impossible for families to leave the country. Varnero described the way his love for the country that had given his family so much had now led to them losing the most important thing: their freedom.

After years of enduring the hardships imposed by the regime, his company had won a contract to asphalt the main road from Addis Ababa to Djibouti. Following a long construction period, the workers reached the border town of Dewele. The Ethiopian army manning the crossing post gave an order that the mobile camp for the workforce be erected beyond the frontier in Djibouti territory for security reasons – this was an unexpected development, as they had planned to station the camp on the Ethiopian side. This fortuitous change of plans created the opportunity they had been waiting for - a chance to escape.

A team of trusted workers were despatched, on the pretence of renovating their property in Addis Ababa. For two days, they quietly emptied the house of valuables and heirlooms, moving everything in the construction trucks into his older brother's house, as he had decided to remain in the country. It was laborious to organise everything in a way that did not raise suspicion from neighbours who might have been spying on them. They were thus running the risk of being reported to the authorities. Fortunately, things went smoothly, and the escape plan was set for the following day.

Late that afternoon, the company double cab Fiat OM truck arrived at the house. At the rear of the truck under a soft dark canvas, machinery was stocked up for the long journey. The family disguised themselves in scruffy work overalls and joined the workers on the track. As they encountered roadblocks along the way, they genuinely had to appear as though they were heading towards to the construction site. At this point in the story, Varnero looked me dead in the eyes, with all seriousness, and stressed that if they had been caught, they would have found themselves incarcerated, or God knows what else.

They set off for the long drive after 7 p.m., as they believed it would be easier to drive at night to avoid soldiers. Luckily, they were stopped just once, some hours from Addis Ababa, and without fuss, after greasing the soldier's palm, they were allowed to proceed. It was a perilous drive of nearly ten hours, but they finally reached the proximity of the mobile camp at dawn. They stopped, set up camp some miles before the town of Dewele, and waited for nightfall before to make the final move.

Under the cover of darkness, the truck reached the border and more workers were loaded with a permit pass that was obtained for the vehicle. Somehow undetected, the family crossed the checkpoint into Djibouti and on to freedom, together.

Varnero and I sat together for hours as he unfolded his extraordinary tale of endurance. When he finished, he asked me eagerly about my personal views on the future of the islands and local politics, and if he should invest his money here with me. I knew, no matter what the cost, that I had to be honest with him. I told him of my fears and growing loss of confidence in the Seychelles since the last attempted coup. At this moment in time, there simply were not enough construction projects in the country that could justify any new investment. He appreciated my straight talk and understandably reached the conclusion that a one-party socialist state was not the right country in which to invest.

Chapter fifty four

The Morning of Thursday, 12 July 1982

Nello had planned a trip to Hong Kong for the purpose of acquiring some new stock of ivory and coral jewellery for his shop. Helena and I decided to join him on the trip to take a break from our tumultuous life in paradise. We took advantage of the weekly British Airways flight and booked ourselves a room at the Hong Kong Hotel by Kowloon Harbour. Landing at Kai Tak airport was quite a dramatic and frightening experience, as described by many – Hong Kong airport was, at the time, ranked the sixth most dangerous airport in the world. Its geographic location, surrounded by rugged mountains and Victoria Harbour, meant that the only way to land was to turn sharply at low altitude once the plane reached the multi-storey buildings of Kowloon, with just a short stretch before touchdown and a very short runway that ended in the sea. Pilots found this technically demanding.

While Nello went on his shopping spree, we joined travellers' trails visiting the sights and leisurely enjoying our freedom. The cosmopolitan city seemingly never slept. Neon signs of all different sizes and shapes flashed everywhere in vivid colours to attract the attention of passers-by. The nightlife was intense with nightclubs, bars, pubs, and restaurants that featured mainly Cantonese cuisine, but also some western, including Italian, of course!

The football World Cup finals were taking place in Spain at the time. I was not able to follow the tournament, especially since in the Seychelles we received news a week late. On the morning of Thursday 12 July, on our way to the breakfast we were greeted by a loud, exhilarated hotel staff; they wanted to shake our hands, and they congratulated us triumphantly. We could not comprehend what was going on until finally one of the managers asked if we had watched the World Cup final last night. After seeing no reaction, he announced that Italy had won. Bang. It clicked. 'We' were world champions. I suddenly felt proud to be Italian. It seemed unreal that people could be so euphoric and happy for us in a foreign country. I joined in the chanting and cheering, sharing their happiness. Italy had beaten West Germany 3-1, against all the odds. We did not know if we were the only Italians at the hotel, but it sounded like they all knew, and everyone greeted us with great passion and love.

Chapter fifty five

The Mutineers

The soldiers based at Union Vale, just north of Victoria, had consistently complained of the poor living conditions at their garrison. It had once been the colonial prison and had been adapted to accommodate the soldiers under Tanzanian command. However, the buildings were unfitted for their purpose and the soldiers lived in squalid, inhumane conditions. They were also expected to guard the hundreds of political detainees that occupied cells in an equally undignified and dreadful state.

When their complaints fell upon deaf ears, a rebellion was hatched by junior officers and disgruntled soldiers. Some 300 soldiers took part in the protest against the senior office command. What was initially a series of complaints resulted in a mutiny.

On 22 August 1982, the mutineers took control of the radio station, the port, the central police station and the Cable & Wireless building. Their leader said on the radio they had been 'treated like pigs' by the officers in charge and demanded they be removed and replaced. The soldiers wanted respect and better living conditions for themselves and the detainees at the barracks.

Without any warning, our morning routine was interrupted by the ensuing mayhem. At the office, my secretary Labonté was like a frenzied madman, blaming the regime; it was every man for himself. Helena made her way back home too. It was still daylight so we could see what was going on – the frenetic rush of army vehicles crossing the roads and soldiers posted in strategic locations across town. Victoria had become a battlefield, as the mutineer soldiers tried to defend and control their occupied positions and those loyal to René fought to regain order.

Returning back home to St Louis, I was in danger of getting caught in the crossfire as I drove right through the middle of town. I kept going in the hope that they would not shoot at civilian cars trying to get to safety. As I reached St Louis, Seychelles Radio, occupied by the mutineers, transmitted a message from the rebel leader to stay home. Another curfew was imposed upon the country. We were shocked by the intensity of the gunfire that seemed to last for hours.

Mere was alone in the house when she saw our cars parked and decided to check if we were safe. She gradually walked down the hill – at her age, she was a slow walker. By the time she reached us, agitated, and puffing heavily, she was troubled by the shooting and the noise of firearms. She appeared at the door, trembling like a tree branch during a windy storm, whispering words in Creole as she entered the living room. She looked weird and Helena asked if she was well. We noticed some large prominent cotton balls sticking out of her ears, one pink and the other white on each side. She had used some of her homemade tampons to shield her ears from the noise of the guns and looked hilarious. Even with all the seriousness of the commotion we were in, we could not help ourselves and, as our eyes met, we both burst into laughter at how silly she looked.

Fierce gunfire continued for two days. President René crushed the revolt with the help of foreign military intervention. The Tanzanian army came to the rescue and more than 40 mutineers were captured and arrested. Eight people died, including six soldiers and two civilians. The Seychellois were traumatised by the unfortunate event and an around-the-clock curfew was imposed for several days.

The event was another huge setback for the Praslin Beach Resort project; the furnishing and equipment plan was now in disarray and the hotel stood empty. In fact, this further added to the litany of events that alienated the shareholders and destroyed their confidence about investment in the country. And, in response, my confidence wavered, too.

Chapter fifty six

Eroded Friendship

In Ricci's books, Guy Morel was a highly sought-after person because of his position in the government. Ricci tried hard to bring him under his control, to woo him with dinner parties and the occasional gift. We saw Guy more often, at dinner parties or at home. After Sue left for England, he started a relationship with a Praslinoise, Jenny, who owned a beautiful boutique resort in Praslin, La Reserve.

One Sunday at lunch at his house in Ma Constance, Guy asked me about Mario Ricci. Before I replied, I decided to sound out his interest in him. He had been seeing him frequently and had become fond of him, he said. They liked each other – 'He seems a good and reliable friend' – he added. I hesitated at this, and then told him of my initial experiences. I added that, from what I knew, he had behaved honestly and honourably with SOGIS and Floris's deals, but dubiously with Signor Cossu's affairs. I emphasised his questionable background, saying he sounded like a potentially dangerous mafioso.

Guy was regularly in Praslin, commuting at the weekends. A large plot of farmland on the island with a beautiful old plantation house became available on the market. The property was unique, and the present owner was looking a quick cash deal. Unable to personally finance the deal, Guy turned to Ricci for a loan. After my previous warnings, I was shocked to hear that he had decided to get financially involved with him. Guy believed that because of their friendship, Ricci would no doubt, in time, write off the loan.

A few months went by, but it was not long before Ricci started to ask him for favours. Guy would not give in to his requests to reform financial restrictions in order to facilitate his businesses. Their friendship cooled down after Guy refused to cooperate with his schemes. In the end, Guy decided to terminate their relationship by forfeiting the property, as there was no way he could repay the loan. He had come to terms with my early warnings about the man and his intentions, but he was glad that the short-lived friendship ended before it really began. For Ricci, it was just a case of one door closing but another one opening as his alliances continuously changed.

Chapter fifty seven

A New Venture

With the continuing volatility and uncertainty surrounding the business and my future in the Seychelles, I hesitated in deciding what to do next. An Italian entrepreneur had become a regular visitor to the Seychelles and my Victoria office. We started talking business when he suggested that I work for him in Italy. He wanted to establish an import and export company and asked me to help kick-start the business.

My new interlocutor was very keen to have me on board with his new planned venture and told me he had the financial backing of two other friends. I was torn about what to do. I wanted stability and realised this could not be like the blind date scenario of my first arrival in the Seychelles. I drew up an employment contract with hefty demands, expecting a rejection, but it turned out they accepted my proposal. Unbelievable!

Funnily enough, I was not overjoyed, only disappointed. It was strange how I reacted to what normally should have been an achievement. But I could not back down and was left with the huge task of announcing my decision to Mr Floris.

I travelled to Sardinia to face the music, arranging an appointment at his office. I was still rather disturbed about my decision. In the end, I began to see it as an act of independence and freedom that would allow me to follow my own inspiration.

Mr Floris did not take the news very well; he was incredulous, saying that he wanted me to stay on his payroll no matter what, even offering me a job in Sardinia. I had to reason with him and explain myself; it was not an easy decision to leave him. The Seychelles affair and present status quo of his financial disinvestment was leaving me unmotivated and let down.

We both got emotional and, in the end, I promised him that I would not abandon ship. I would still look after his business in the Seychelles from my office in Italy. He liked that compromise. I felt like I was 17 years old again, making the decision to leave Dad's vineyards. This was another milestone in my life.

In early February 1983, I moved to Tuscany. Having avoided winters for six years, on a dull, wintry, and wet day I checked in at the Hermitage Hotel in Poggio a Caiano, a quaint little town halfway between Florence and Pistoia, and quite a contrast to the sunny Seychelles.

The three partners in the new project were each individually successful businessmen. They were buying a huge variety of manufactured goods, electrical appliances, and electronic gadgets from Italian wholesalers. The new company would be importing all the merchandise directly from abroad, bypassing wholesalers and boosting their profits handsomely. Their sale depots were strategically located in the triangular area of Viareggio, Pisa, and Pistoia, rich with manufacturing and trade – an ideal base.

Under my management, we would acquire the goods they needed. It was a thriving operation from the start. Business trips took me frequently to the Far East, Hong Kong, and Taiwan, but also back to the Seychelles as needed, along with London and Sardinia.

The success of the operation created a frenzy of opportunities and made me eager to expand my activities. I was to travel to Gabon to explore a potential million-dollar business deal proposed by the Gabonese government to supply prefabricated dwellings in exchange for manganese, oil or timber. This would have been an extraordinary deal, but we had neither the financing nor the infrastructure to deliver results.

It turned out that the goods that arrived in containers were being despatched into sale depots unequally as the purchases were also unevenly funded. This meant that only one particular business partner made a profit, creating antipathy and animosity among the others.

Helena remained in the Seychelles, and we had to find the right time to communicate during our busy schedules. Due to the erratic telephone service, Helena would arrange to visit the office at Builders Centre and correspond with me using our telex machine, which was used as a premium system separate from the telephone network. To reduce usage of this very costly system, messages were encoded onto a paper tape before being sent online. In this way we kept in touch regularly. I was missing her terribly!

In the business, the three friends had started in earnest to argue and quibble. I found myself in the middle of continuous disputes and arguments among the shareholders. I was exhausted by travelling across the globe and could not relax and enjoy the fruit of my achievements.

Seven months later, I had had enough; I could not be persuaded to remain. I quit and travelled back to the Seychelles, feeling like I had never really left.

Chapter fifty eight

To Fly International

The many attempts to overthrow René, along with the army mutiny, repeatedly brought the Seychelles into the global news for the wrong reasons. It was continuously reported that the country was an unsafe travel destination and consequently, after the airport damages and resulting temporary closure following the mercenaries' ambush, foreign airlines stopped flying to the islands as it was deemed too costly to insurance the operation. Demand collapsed; tourists declined to a critical level, with grave economic consequences for the country as foreign currency earnings vanished.

The government had to act, and it took the unprecedented decision to make its domestic airline fly internationally. It was a gamble. Guy Morel also assumed the role of chairman of this new initiative.

Air Seychelles had a domestic fleet of small propeller aircrafts such as the Britten-Norman Trislander, a BN2 Islander and Short 360 in use to link Mahé with Praslin, Bird and Denis Island, but no proper equipment or crew to fly internationally. The government lacked financial resources and the only way to achieve this goal was to find an airline that would fly the European service on their behalf, a ready-to-fly operation. By contracting in such a way, the operating airline would provide the aircraft, crew, maintenance, and insurance, along with all direct costs such as fuel, catering, airport fees, handling and navigation fees. Passengers' tickets sales and cargo became Air Seychelles' straightforward revenue.

Bravely, the government signed a contract for a basic airline charter with British Caledonian using one of their McDonnell Douglas DC-10 wide-bodied aircrafts to fly weekly from London Gatwick to Mahé via Frankfurt under the Air Seychelles flight number. The operation began in October 1983, restoring direct links to Europe and bringing tourists back to the shores of the Seychelles.

I was invited to the opening reception at Gatwick airport for its first maiden flight; it was a gathering packed with glitzy personalities along with British and European journalists. Some were there just for the reception and others were flying as government guests to the Seychelles.

I met with Sandro Paternostro there, the London correspondent of the Italian television channel, RAI. I had seen him many times on the Italian TV news as a child; he was an icon of my generation. He was travelling to the Seychelles for the first time and our chat turned into an interview. Paternostro was writing an editorial about the Seychelles for *il Giorno* and questioned me about the country's politics and the coup. I avoided his line of questioning and talked solely about the beauty and charm of my paradise islands and still relatively undiscovered tropical archipelago. It was of vital importance that this government venture was fruitful as the financial risk was enormous for a small country of only 80,000 inhabitants.

The gamble paid off; the operation turned out to be remarkably successful as more flights were planned to new destinations. It also served the purpose of restoring confidence to other international airlines that the island was now safe to fly to. This new dawn had brought some positivity to the economy and the country.

Guy suggested that I might be interested in working for the airline as recruitment for managers had begun, but I decided not to pursue the option on offer.

Chapter fifty nine

Moving to England

With shareholder confidence at rock bottom after the military mutiny, I was instructed to wind up and cease SOGIS operations at the Pointe Conan workshop by disposing of all machinery and equipment and selling off remaining stock at the worksite.

The Builder Centre trade business never recovered after the warehouse fire. A local Indian construction company approached us with the intention of acquiring the entire stock along with the land, and we accepted their offer.

I was also instructed to sell the Praslin resort, which was owned by a separate development company, with Mr Floris still the major shareholder. I contacted various real estate agents in England and Italy in search of a possible buyer or management company, but this arduous task proved fruitless due to the political climate, as no one wanted to engage in new business in the Seychelles. We had no alternative but to wait for better circumstances. Buying time, we kept on a small workforce to provide maintenance and upkeep.

In October 1983, I travelled to London, with the intention of creating my own business and settling down with Helena to start a family. It was just a question of where and what sector I wished to be involved in. I had visited London on business trips over the last few years and noticed the transformation that the country had undergone since my student days in the early 1970s. The city was buzzing with opportunities, flourishing with new communities, and embracing its cultural diversity. In my opinion, joining the European Community had been fruitful. London was no longer isolated or wrapped up in British sentiments and was now a city that belonged to the world. I decided, after much assessment of my options, that London was the right place to start my very own business in the travel industry.

Helena joined me in England. I kept travelling in and out of the Seychelles to tie up loose ends and for family holidays.

Unexpectedly, on 7 April 1984, we received an official notice of a compulsory acquisition from the Ministry of National Development. The Seychelles Government, exercising new powers, had confiscated the Praslin Beach resort for one rupee, or four pence. I had warned Mr Floris that this might happen, as land was being confiscated from local exiled landowners who were against René's regime, and I had been told by local sources that foreign investment properties that were not operating could be a target for seizure. I petitioned, with the company's board, to get the hotel back and running, but Mr Floris had lost interest and trust in the Seychelles government and persuaded the remaining shareholders to follow his judgment that there should be no further investment until they could regain some trust.

These instructions stunned the shareholders, and they were confronted with the helpless dilemma of what to do next. I was asked by Mr Floris on behalf of the board to take care of the business at hand. This was beyond my usual job role, an unforeseeable task. Reluctantly, I was persuaded to take charge, as I had been the face of the company for years.

I returned to the Seychelles to assess the situation and submit an objection, together with a formal claim. I attempted a friendly approach with the authorities, but soon enough I realised that there was no room to manoeuvre; it was a non-starter. My connections were unwilling to get involved and/or powerless to do so.

Accepting the status quo was not an option. I took the

unprecedented decision to sue the Seychelles government in a court of law. I wondered if I was having a moment of madness. No one had dared to object to a compulsory acquisition in court, as the president appointed all magistrates and juridical staff. By challenging a dictatorial regime in its own court of law, I was risking deportation, physical harm, or worse.

Living on the edge in paradise for seven years had taught me resilience in the face of many difficult situations; I was no longer the naïve new kid on the block. I resolved that this would be my greatest challenge yet.

My task of finding a solicitor to represent us in court proved fruitless, as local law firms were concerned about possible retributions for taking on such a case. Eventually, through business connections, I managed to recruit an Indian solicitor from Madras. Mr Navaratnam would travel to the Seychelles and together we would prepare for the case. We had plenty of time to gather evidence and testimonies for our deposition as the showdown court case was set for October 1986, in two years' time.

A week before the trial, I apprehensively travelled back to the Seychelles, full of trepidation. Taking the stand in court was not wise and I knew that the eyes of the regime were on me; informers were crawling in the courthouse like cockroaches. After four days, the case was adjourned to the following month. To my and everybody else's surprise, I received no threats or harassments, although I remained alert and vigilant throughout my short stays. It was not until October 13, 1987, almost a year later, that the Supreme Court finally delivered a verdict.

We were extremely disappointed with the result – while we had targeted at least half of the valuation, we were awarded only a fraction of what the resort was worth. We had, nevertheless, achieved a victory. Challenging the government in court was unheard of and our good fortune could now make it possible for others to do the same.

An appeal was suggested, but the shareholders decided against it, as the situation was fragile, and it would be time consuming and, perhaps, fail to deliver a better result. Taking everything into consideration, I accepted the compensation on behalf of the company. The experience had been exasperating but it was now over, and I was alive and unharmed.

The Praslin Beach Hotel opened its doors soon after, initially under a parastatal management company, only to be sold by the government to a Malaysian company for millions of dollars. It turned out to be an extraordinarily successful and profitable hotel operation.

Following the verdict by the Supreme Court on the Praslin Beach properties, the business affairs of Mr Floris finally came to an end. Soon after, I accompanied him to tie up these activities, as he still owned shares in the Ocean Gate House and wanted to dispose of them. We stayed, deliberately, at one of the properties owned by Ricci in Mahé, the Danzille Hotel at Bel Ombre. Ricci had moved his headquarters there and we met with him to finalise the sale of Floris's shares. It was a respectable business-like transaction, smooth and direct. Mr Floris remarked on how powerful Ricci had become in the Seychelles. Truly remarkable, I agreed.

We stayed for the whole week and, with the business out of the way, we enjoyed the beach and snorkelled for shells. Even Mrs Floris relished my company; perhaps she had come to terms with the fact that I was now no longer financially dependent on them. Her views about me had improved remarkably since our trip around the Far East. She even openly asked for my opinions and cherished them. I hoped that our relationship would remain after everything settled down, as Mr Floris inspired me greatly and I had always admired him and given him the utmost respect.

Chapter sixty

Coup Attempt

I started my new travel agency in the West End of London, keeping my travels to a minimum so as to direct all my energy towards establishing the business. I was so pleased, and full of enthusiasm for my new venture. I loved making travel itineraries to any destination, whether exotic or less appealing. The business around the neighbourhood was prolific and my clients were varied, from all different professions and backgrounds.

Back in the Seychelles, however, it seemed like nothing had really changed. In July 1986, we heard news of another attempted coup to overthrow René. It felt like a broken record at this point. The news made Helena worried about the continuing volatile situation in the island, as her mum and Guy were still living there.

This time, it seemed more intriguing as, apparently, it was an inside job. Allegedly, the leader of this attempt was René's own minister of defence, Ogilvie Berlouis; it was conceived by a faction of the army under his command. Minister Berlouis was one of René's *paladins* – from humble origins, he had joined René's political party, the Seychelles People's Progressive Front, SPPF, early on. He had originally been sent with a small group of countrymen to train with the Tanzanian army, which turned out to be invaluable as he developed a strong relationship with President Nyerere of Tanzania, who became instrumental to René. René rewarded Berlouis by appointing him minister of defence.

In this role, Berlouis groomed his own circle of friends and rewarded their loyalty with positions within the Ministry and army command. The army unrest and the mutiny had put Berlouis on his toes, encouraged yet again by Ricci!

Ricci had established links with the South African secret services.

The attempted coup turned out to be a web of intrigue that had been spun, involving domestic and foreign governments. The ambiguous relations between the South Africa and Seychelles governments, the South African secret service and Mario Ricci all muddled facts and it was disputable as to who was really involved. The South African secret service nonetheless aborted the coup plot, leaving Ricci to rescue the operation, and become the negotiator and hero in the eyes of René. Seychellois army officers were forced to resign and Berlouis was replaced.

Chapter sixty one

Maintaining Power

Although now living far apart, Guy and Helena became closer as brother and sister. Guy even organised for us to visit the Seychelles one Christmas by arranging air tickets and asking us to stay at his house. He became a regular visitor at our house in England and spent time with us discussing his future projects.

While extremely busy with government affairs and various chairmanships, during his limited spare time, classic music and ballet remained his passions. It had been one of his dreams to bring ballet to the Seychelles. This came to fruition when he succeeded by bringing none other than Rudolf Nureyev for a world-class production of *Giselle*. The Seychellois, for the first time, had the opportunity to experience such a spectacle. Guy was very proud of his achievement for the country.

He was also frustrated and worried by the alliance forming between President René and Ricci. It seemed to be a 'marriage of convenience' and he questioned the direction that the country was moving in. He could not stop talking it about after a glass of wine.

Following the numerous coup attempts that had eroded his trust, President René needed to stay on top of the game and constantly explored the different avenues that were on offer. He played everyone, double-dealing world powers along with his own immediate group of party supporters and inner circle of ministers and officials. He believed a leader must be shrewd, and that it was better to be feared than loved. Ricci had succeeded in convincing René that he had always been a trusted friend and informer, apparently saving his life more than once by uncovering the numerous attempts to overthrown him. Ricci had intriguingly established a business operation in South Africa with local high ranking ex-civil servants, allowing him to engage in relations with the South African intelligence services. This resulted in an extraordinarily complex and sophisticated security protection company specialising in providing the best bodyguard services. A team of special, highly trained bodyguards were dispatched from South Africa to be in charge of René's personal protection and safety.

Their relationship was odd, but René apparently found Ricci fascinating and Machiavellian in the way he conducted business and in his behaviour. Both used any means necessary to maintain political power – the end always justified the means (*la fine giustifica i mezzi*) no matter how cruel, manipulative, and immoral those means might be. Ricci was a sort of genius insinuator for René's regime and René rewarded Ricci with what he wanted most — a free hand to do as he pleased in the country.

In the middle 1980s, the government passed legislation that would enable it to become a fiscal paradise, allowing offshore companies to be legalised and registered in the country, starting at the end of that decade. A joint venture between Ricci and the Seychelles government was created exclusively for this purpose, under the banner of the Seychelles Trust Company.

The Seychelles became the first socialist tax haven in the world. With the oil embargo in South Africa, an intricate network of companies was registered to break the capital-imposed boycott, bypass trade sanctions and facilitate the movement of prohibited goods through the Seychelles, assisting the South African government in avoiding the economic sanctions. Ricci was the mastermind of the country's offshore business.

According to *radio bambou*, under Ricci's spell, the country became a haven for illicit business, a home to financial criminality and money-laundering. Illegitimate businessmen found easy pastures in Ricci's network of cover-up businesses, attracting dirty money from around the world. Ricci and René's entourage used a network of shell companies, clandestine trusts and frontmen to channel millions of pounds overseas.

As a result, Ricci amassed a great deal of power in the country. He was seen as René's deputy and even gained diplomatic status. However, he failed to make Italian the fourth official language of the Seychelles, as he had originally demanded. His career progressed nonetheless, and his connections multiplied across all levels, with the influence of the South African government as well as in the underground world of organised crime. The Seychelles became his adopted country, and because of its size, he easily found fresh territory to effortlessly corrupt officials. His influence permitted him free access to literally anything he desired.

Ricci gave refuge to a number of individuals with dubious backgrounds, hosting them personally. He chased his objectives voraciously, using contacts he had made during his career to create a portfolio of clients.

He became a chameleon who could fit in with anyone, anywhere. Within the Seychelles, he had acquired an extreme sense of self-importance, and an aura of intrigue surrounded him. A widely respected dealmaker among his long list of foreign clients, Ricci was also a complicated person, and his power depended on his ability to deal tough. Oddly, he was rarely seen in public, exclusively frequenting his close circles of contacts.

I thought about the morning when Ricci had arrived in the Seychelles from Mogadishu; he had appeared to be an ordinary man, almost insignificant in stature. After a few years, Ricci had become influential and powerful. An Italian proverb says '*l'abito non fa il monaco*' (which translates as 'it is not the cowl that makes the monk'). René and Ricci formed an odd couple indeed, as Guy often remarked. Ultimately, by deciding to stay out of politics, Guy had served the nation as best as he could!

Chapter sixty two

Air Sardinia

Back in Italy, Signor Cossu's self-catering business, a partnership with a local businessman at his former farm, went bankrupt and the property was confiscated for auction by a court order. After enjoying his extravagant life at full speed, Cossu's fortunes were diminishing fast.

The Seychelles government paid him cash for the airlines, and he settled the Pirates Arms property in treasury bonds, payable in half-yearly instalments over a ten-year period. He was worried about the Seychelles Taxation Office possibly seizing the bonds due to his outstanding taxes. He came up with a scheme to establish a regional airline with bases in the secondary airports of Sardinia.

On the Isle of Wight in England, he visited the headquarters of Britten-Norman, manufacturers of the Islander aircraft. He had previously dealt with the company while in the Seychelles under Inter Island Airways. He managed to convert the Seychelles treasure bonds into a 'today deal', exchanging them for a second-hand Islander aircraft.

Air Sardinia, Signor Cossu's newest adventure, was born in 1987. He had the aircraft registered and named LILY after his wife. With new livery painted on the aircraft, he now presented himself as a serious and trusted investor.

He went in search of investors prepared to support his new project. He got the local media involved and his adventurous life story, charisma and savoir-faire were an easy sell with local backers. What followed was an over-subscription of shares, but of course, Cossu had no problem with that. Investors were seduced by his sweet talk and his lavish pitch. He made it seem like his start-up airline business with the one small propeller aircraft would be the next Pan Am!

Air Sardinia got its licence to start operations initially by flying regionally in Sardinia. Gradually, they began to fly to mainland Italian airports, striking a deal to become a feeder for Alitalia. Unbelievably, Cossu once again had a business up and running. Air Sardinia expanded with three more aircrafts joining the fleet, a Cessna 412B twin engine and two Fairchild Metroliner aircrafts. He revived operations in Oristano, bought the Arbatax airfield and housed his office headquarters at a prominent location in Cagliari.

His delusions of grandeur were infectious. The stakeholder meetings were staged in beautiful surroundings with members flown into exclusive locations and entertained to the max. This was a luxury reserved only for successful and profitable businesses. I visited Cossu at his opulent office headquarters in Cagliari, where he even had his own private apartment above his office. This was typical of him! He wanted me to be part of his new enterprise.

He invited me for lunch one day when he was visiting London. He was staying in the presidential suite at the Sheraton Tower in Knightsbridge. He offered me a position to represent Air Sardinia in the UK as their general sales agent. I accepted this new appointment, as he asked for nothing in return. We had a sumptuous lunch that he paid for with his brand-new Air Sardinia Amex card; I noticed it had a chairman imprint. I had to admit, I was impressed; he was like a cat with nine lives. We kept in touch afterwards. He insisted that, from then on, I should call him Corrado instead of Signor Cossu.

Soon enough, Air Sardinia ran out of cash and the debts started to quickly accumulate. The company did not generate enough income to support the ever-increasing overheads; Corrado was literally burning through cash to support his flamboyant lifestyle. His way of conducting business was unorthodox and his mismanagement was too obvious – the company was bound for failure.

After the company had been in trouble for some time, Corrado hoped the regional government would inject fresh funds. His financial position was deteriorating fast. The shareholders had got scared and wanted out.

In 1990, Corrado travelled to Houston, Texas to visit a mutual friend from the Seychelles, Peter Ward. Peter ran the office of Halpern & Woolf, an auditor's firm. He had moved to establish a Houston branch for the firm after the trouble escalated in Mahé. He had also helped Corrado settle his outstanding business in the Seychelles.

While in Texas, Corrado mentioned his ill health and after visiting a specialist, he was recommended for a heart bypass operation. The surgery went well but, while he was recovering in Texas away from indiscreet eyes, Air Sardinia shut its operations and was declared bankrupt, just three years after it had been launched.

Deluded investors had lost an enormous amount of money in the venture; some were glad that it ended because the debt vacuum had been increasing exponentially. Months later, Peter cut ties with him following a disputed business agreement that Corrado never honoured.

Chapter sixty three

Italia 1990

In 1990, Italy was the host nation for the World Cup final, with the tournament scheduled between 8 June and 8 July, just in the middle of the summer holiday season.

England was confined to playing its preliminary matches in Cagliari on Sardinia because of the issue of hooliganism. This was a cause of concern for the travel business as, even before the tournament started, newspaper headlines were full of reports of violent behaviour by the fans, suggesting they might disrupt the holiday season. On the other hand, this was an opportunity to show the rest of the world the beauty of the island in the middle of the summer, putting it on the map as a holiday destination for the English market.

The preparation and logistics of moving thousands of fans was enormous and unbelievably strenuous. Airlines were chartered, hotel rooms and coaches were booked, and fans were subjected to scrutiny at the airports as a way to weed out the thugs. During the tournament, the headlines were full of bad news with fans trashing bars and hotel rooms, along with nightly stand-offs with the local police and other disruptive social behaviour. As the tournament moved on to the mainland, peace returned to the island. The holiday season ended on a higher note for us and, despite it all, the English media enthusiastically discovered the beautiful island of Sardinia.

The following summer season, we exclusively contracted our first direct flight service in partnership with British Airways, flying at civilised hours from London Heathrow to Cagliari in the south and Olbia on the north-west coast of Sardinia. It was a full service complete with business class on board. We were the first and only tour operator flying these routes, and fighting back against the perception that charters operated at odd times, in old aircrafts with no catering service, from uncomfortable airports. This became our core business, as we introduced more flights for the Christmas and Easter holidays as well to complement our summer programme.

Finally, the Sardinian community in England had the opportunity to fly back home in just over two hours, instead of what used to be a six-hour journey with a connecting flight via the mainland.

New opportunities opened up for my travel business and I fully exploited my options. Our flying operation expanded as we provided the only direct flights connecting Sardinia with the UK. This gave us the upper hand in providing the best holiday packages to Sardinia. As I was busy with the growth, I limited my trips to Sardinia, which were mostly for business.

Chapter sixty four

Betrayed

In 1991, Guy unexpectedly turned up at our home in England; it was unusual for him, and he was not on government business. A year or so before, President René had asked him to retire from his post and to accept a role as his personal advisor, retaining all his government perks, along with his diplomatic passport. Guy liked the idea of this new role and the freedom it would give him to pursue other interests and activities. But it was not to last; René reneged on his words and cancelled all the arrangements and privileges. Guy felt betrayed by the man he had loyally served for many years. To René, 'Each person served his purpose and was then disposed of,' Guy claimed. He was cross with René's ever-changing behaviour and even thought about challenging him in future elections.

In September, no longer with the administration, Guy formed the Seychelles Management Institute and a Tutorial College for underprivileged children. He was a keen visionary, giving the less fortunate a chance to excel through free education, and a firm believer in the importance of education to motivate people to build a successful society. He recognised that the country needed to provide a versatile system of education, as different people had different abilities. He was not enthusiastic about the Creole dialect being formally introduced in schools because of its limited use beyond the islands' shores and felt that resources were better spent in improving the standards of English teaching at schools. He started to compile a series of books designed to improve the students' English language skills with a view towards refining accuracy, and thus inspiring confidence and professionalism.

Fresh winds swept the world in early 1990s., notably the dissolution of the Soviet Union after years of perestroika. The ripples were felt around the world, especially in sovereign nations who were economically dependent on the USSR. President René could no longer rely on Russia's support and was forced to change his political strategy, approaching Western nations. However, these governments put pressure on René to change his policies in order to make the country compliant with international financial rules and to return the nation to a multi-party state.

Following René's new strategy, Mario Ricci permanently resettled in South Africa. Mr James Mancham, the ousted former president, was allowed back into the Seychelles, ahead of the new election planned for 1993. A sense of freedom and liberation swept the country.

Looking back on my time in Seychelles, I realise that I had lived my original dream: a young man who wanted experience the world, passionately pursuing any commitments and responsibilities laid out before him. Certainly, I had not anticipated the tumultuous nature of these years and often got more than I bargained for. With reflection, I became stronger and grew to better myself afterwards; the experience had helped to improve my self-confidence and self-esteem, allowing me to face adversity in every situation. The multiple business scenarios I experienced made me release my potential and increase my determination to move forward without depending on others, being in full command of my ship, steering it in the direction of my choosing.

However, my years in the Seychelles were the best of my life. As a foreigner to the country, I was fortunate to experience these untouched islands, its people, its culture, and the mesmerizing, lush natural landscapes and seashores. I am grateful that I had the opportunity to see it all.

I still remember having teary eyes on the plane when leaving the Seychelles and how exuberantly happy I was every time I returned.

What the Seychelles may lack in size, it makes up for in personality. It is an independent nation that has gone through so much change in a relatively short space of time but has remained resilient and determined to succeed in adversity.

Chapter sixty five

Mama's Spaghetti

My parents had been looking forward to my return from the Seychelles, hoping that I would finally settle down in Terralba. It is a common desire of many parents that one of their offspring will take care of them in their old age. However, I had other plans and wanted to settle down in London. This would have been a disappointment for my parents, but they only wished to see me succeed, even if it meant breaking their hearts in the process. After all, Terralba had changed greatly because of the economic crisis of 1980-90 through which it suffered a big downturn. Many operations had gone out of business, although the town remained tranquil: certainly not as vibrant as London life.

Babbu and I spoke often, and we enjoyed each other's company and conversation. My teenage anger had gone a long time earlier. I had purchased a projector and, when I was at home, I would share images with my parents of all my travels around the world. They were delighted to hear the story behind each picture. My visits were always followed by tearful farewells and embraces at every departure.

Uncharacteristically, Babbu had become more interested in me as an entrepreneur, and he was also proud of my tenacity and courage. He immensely respected the way I acted maturely and responsibly in creating my new business in London on my own. He understood the risks I was taking in chartering aircrafts throughout the summer months and admired my ways of expanding the business. He finally came to believe in me, and we reconciled our differences, accepting each other's opinions as father and son.

I eventually managed to fly Mama to visit us in London, in the summer of 1990, using our direct flight. Unfortunately, Babbu was unable to fly due to his medical condition. At the age of 70, Mama had fulfilled her dream of flying on a plane and travelling abroad for the first time.

Sadly, Babbu passed away just before Easter, in April 1992, at the age of 79. It was unexpected; Helena and I had planned to visit Sardinia for the Easter break. His death left me with a big hole in my life. I reflect on him often; he was a good man and father, and I missed him dearly. I wished I had taken more time to tell him that I loved him and, most of all, that I had always respected him for who he was. He had always wanted us to be prepared and to toughen up for the life that lay ahead of us. He tried his best to pass on all his life experience in the only way he knew how. As his son, I would describe my father's character as being like an egg, with a tough outer shell and a soft inside; it was hard to find a way to get inside without breaking the egg. He probably felt that he could not or would not show his tenderness. Regrettably, my children never got the chance to get to know him. He would have been a great *nonno*.

After my father's death, Mama was free of any commitments at home and, now on her own, she joined a group of ladies from the local church who travelled on religious trips across Italy, including a pilgrimage to Lourdes in France. Her free spirit developed and evolved. At every opportunity, she would fly and visit us in England as often she could. And, even when she was told that pasta was now widely available in the UK supermarkets, she was still determined to carry her favourite Barilla *spaghetti* in her suitcase.

Lightning Source UK Ltd.
Milton Keynes UK
UKHW041208160222
398775UK00001B/59